This Book Belongs
To: Marlene
Stanton

D1214901

Sing Praise

Sing Praise

HYMNAL FOR THE DEAF

BROADMAN PRESS
Nashville, Tennessee

© Copyright 1975 BROADMAN PRESS
Nashville, Tennessee
All rights reserved
International Copyright Secured
4500-14

Printed in the United States of America

Preface

This collection of interpreted versions of hymns has been compiled to meet the needs of the growing number of deaf worshipers and to assist interpreters with the musical aspects of the church's ministry to the deaf. The contents of this hymnal are the result of work done by a hymnal committee composed of Mrs. Louis A. Beard, interpreter, Houston, Texas; William E. Davis, accomplished musician, former pastor to the deaf, and now superintendent of the Tennessee School for the Deaf, Knoxville, Tennessee; and Carter Bearden, missionary to the deaf, Home Mission Board, Atlanta, Georgia.

The hymnal committee expresses its thanks to L. D. Wood, former assistant director, Department of Language Missions of the Home Mission Board, Atlanta, Georgia, and to William J. Reynolds, secretary of the Church Music Department, Sunday School Board of the Southern Baptist Convention, Nashville, Tennessee, for their work in making the publication of this hymnal possible; to Theodore DeLaney of the Lutheran Church, Missouri Synod, for his invaluable suggestions; and to Bill F. Leach, Terry Kirkland, and other personnel of the Church Music Department of the Sunday School Board for their contributions to the publication of this hymnal.

It is our hope and prayer that this first collection of hymns for the deaf published by the Southern Baptist Convention will be most helpful to those who interpret, and a great blessing to deaf worshipers wherever they gather in His name.

Mrs. Louis A. Beard
William E. Davis
Carter Bearden, *Chairman*

Using the Hymnal

The hymns in *Sing Praise* have been interpreted in AMES-LAN (American Sign Language) and consequently do not follow the exact words as sung by the hearing congregation. This departure from normal English syntax has been made in order to clearly convey the meaning of the hymns to the deaf worshiper.

Capitalized words such as HE, HIM, YOU, and YOUR, speak of God and should be signed "Godward." Personal pronouns such as I, ME, and MY, should be signed in a way to show clearly whether they refer to God or Jesus or to the individual worshiper.

The word "presence" is used in many hymns to replace the word "before." To make the sign for "presence," bring your opened left hand in front of you, palm toward yourself. At the same time bring the opened right hand, palm facing forward, toward the left hand, leaving a three- or four-inch space between the palms. An experienced interpreter can help you give a correct rendition of this and other signs presented in this book.

The footnotes following each hymn provide alternative signing suggestions for additional clarity and simplification. AMES-LAN verbs—to be, and helping verbs—are also given in the footnotes throughout the book.

All the hymns in this collection have been selected from *Baptist Hymnal,* 1975. *Sing Praise* is available in two editions: a bound edition and a loose-leaf edition. The loose-leaf edition may be inserted into the loose-leaf edition of *Baptist Hymnal,* 1975, providing a copy of both the music as the hearing congregation sings it and the interpreted versions for signing by the deaf. Each hymn has also been cross-referenced, giving the hymn number for *Baptist Hymnal,* 1975; *Baptist Hymnal,* 1956; and *Broadman Hymnal.*

Two indexes are provided for *Sing Praise.* The Index of First Lines and Titles lists the titles of the hymns, as well as the first line of each hymn where the title and the first line are not identical. In every instance the first line used in the Index is the first line as it appears in *Baptist Hymnal,* 1975, rather than the first line of the interpreted version. The Topical Index corresponds with the Topical Index in *Baptist Hymnal,* 1975, to facilitate the use of the signing version of the hymns with the singing version.

Interpreting Church Music

Music has always played a significant role in the worship of God. Three fourths of the books of the Bible refer to music in some way. The inclusion of the psalms in the Old Testament indicates the importance God's chosen people placed on praising God through music, for the book of Psalms was the songbook of the Hebrews. They called it by a word that means "Songs of Praise." From that time to this day, the people of God have loved and made great use of music in worship.

Music can be as important to the deaf worshiper as it is to the hearing worshiper if the signing of the hymns is done with as much beauty and meaning as possible. The signing should be rhythmic and flowing, and the finger spelling reduced to a minimum. Spelling should be used only when necessary to convey meaning.

Good signing of church music comes only after much work and practice. The interpreter who leads the deaf in singing has the same need to prepare himself as the music director and choir who lead the hearing congregation. Preparation is imperative if music for the deaf is to be clear and meaningful.

Four areas of study will be of value to interpreters of church music:

1. *English Language.*—A good interpreter must be a student of the English language. It is impossible to translate something into another language until it is clearly understood in its original language and context. This is particularly true in translating church music into the language of signs since the message should be conveyed without the use of finger spelling.

The need for clarity and understanding can be illustrated with the gospel song "In Times Like These." One of the lines reads, "In times like these, you need a Savior." If this phrase is signed with no forethought, it may appear that the interpreter is saying, "In clocks like these, you need a Savior." Obviously, a clearer signing would be, "During times like the present, you need a Savior."

In addition to an understanding of words, it is often necessary to analyze the sentence structure of a hymn text in order to sign it with clarity. Finger spelling is necessary in order to sign verbs in the passive voice, but verbs in the active voice are more readily signed without finger spelling. In the hymn "God, Give Us Christian Homes!" for example, almost every line employs verbs in the passive voice. The line that reads "Homes where the Bible is loved and taught" can be changed to "Homes where we love and teach the Bible" to convey the same meaning and eliminate the finger spelling. This approach is desirable in signing hymns.

2. *The Bible.*—A good interpreter must be a student of the Bible. Hymn and anthem texts are filled with theological terminology that must be completely understood before it can be clearly signed. For this reason, every interpreter should have a good Bible dictionary. *The New Bible Dictionary* edited by J. D. Douglas, William B. Eerdman Publishing Company, and *The Laymen's Bible Encyclopedia* by William C. Martin, The Southwestern Company, publishers, are two helpful resources.

In the hymn "I Love Thee," there is an example of problems of theological terminology. The lines that read "Oh, who's like my Savior? He's Salem's bright King" will be difficult to interpret unless the interpreter knows that Salem is a Greek word meaning "safe, at peace." Another good example is "Here I raise mine Ebenezer; Hither by Thy help I'm come" in "Come, Thou Fount of Every Blessing." Neither "raise" nor "Ebenezer" can be signed with meaning unless the interpreter knows that Ebenezer means "stone of help" and that it was erected between Mizpah and Shen by Samuel with the statement, "Hitherto hath the Lord helped us," commemorating Israel's defeat of the Philistines. So "raise" literally means "to establish" or "to build," and "Ebenezer" means something like a monument or an altar which symbolizes God's leadership and help.

Many hymns and anthems have similar quotations and references that will require an understanding of theological terminology if the interpreter is to communicate clearly and accurately.

3. *Language of Signs.*—The interpreter of church music must also be a student of the language of signs. Anyone who has any knowledge of the language of signs is aware that no one ever learns all there is to know about interpreting. The sincere interpreter will continue to grow in his knowledge of the language and in his ability to use it.

One of the problems the interpreter faces is that there is not a wealth of comprehensive material on which he can draw. He has had to depend on others to share their knowledge and experience; for many years this sharing has been the chief source for learning to sign.

With the new social awakening to the deaf population, there has come a demand for materials on manual communication and an increasing flow of books available to interpreters. Several available books are intended to be textbooks for teaching the language of signs. Good books in this field may be obtained from the National Association of the Deaf, Halex House, 814 Thayer Avenue, Silver Springs, Maryland 20910; and Gallaudet College Bookstore, Gallaudet College, Washington, D.C. 20002. David O. Watson's *Talk with Your Hands* may be ordered from the author, Route 1, Winneconne, Wisconsin 54986. Another book of general use to the interpreter is *A Dictionary of Idioms for the Deaf.* Information regarding source and cost may be obtained from the American School for the Deaf, West Hartford, Connecticut.

4. *Musicianship.*—Some interpreters count the measures and try to make the signs fit into the exact pattern of the music. Others suggest that the signs should move upward when the melody ascends and downward when the melody descends. Most interpreters agree, however, that little or no attention needs to be given to the music as it is printed on the page. Rather, the interpreter's concern is to take the music as it is performed and interpret the mood and meaning in the most effective way possible. This means that the interpreter will yield himself to the *feel* and *flow* of the music and *catch* the spirit of the hymn. This must always be done in good taste; never in a distracting way that calls attention to the interpreter rather than the hymn.

It is not vital that an interpreter have a formal or extensive knowledge of music. When a hymn is well interpreted, it will have the general *feel* and *flow* of the music and clearly show the mood and meaning of the text.

In preparing to interpret church music, carefully read the text of the hymn. Do not be satisfied until you are sure of the meaning of every word and phrase. Study the sentence structure of the text. Determine whether there are phrases that should be rearranged or sentences that need to have the verbs changed to active voice. Decide which signs or combinations of signs best convey the meaning of the hymn. Work especially on sections where abstractions are used; determine whether it is better to sign the abstraction exactly as it appears in the language, modify it slightly, or sign the literal meaning. Practice signing hymns before a mirror; polish and perfect the signed form of the song just as carefully as a vocalist polishes and perfects a selection before a performance.

William E. Davis

1. Holy, holy, holy! Lord God all powerful![1]
During morning our songs we offer to YOU;
Holy, holy, holy! Full mercy and power!
God in three Person, Person, Person,[2] wonderful Three in One!

2. Holy, holy, holy! All YOUR people worship YOU,
Putting their golden crowns around YOUR throne;
All heavenly angels kneel before[3] YOU,
Who were[4] and are[5] now and always will continue.

3. Holy, holy, holy! No matter darkness[6] hides YOU,
No matter sinful people YOUR glory can't see,
YOU alone are holy; Truly none holy except YOU,
Perfect in power, in love, and purity.[7]

4. Holy, holy, holy! Lord God all powerful!
All YOUR works shall praise YOUR name on earth, sky, and sea;
Holy, holy, holy! Full mercy and power!
God in three Person, Person, Person, wonderful Three in One!
Amen.

Words, Reginald Heber, 1826.

Make the sign for "power."
Make the sign for "person" three times—one to the left, one in the middle, and one to the right.
Make the sign for "presence," "front," or "face."
Make the sign for "past."
Make the sign for "truly."
Make the sign for "dark."
Make the sign for "clean" with the right "P" hand, palm facing down.

1. Rejoice,[1] you pure in heart,
   Rejoice, give thanks and sing;
   Your glorious[2] flag wave high,
   Cross HIS Christ your King.

2. Smart youth[3] and white-haired age,[4]
   Strong men and women pretty,
   Offer your free happy song,
   God's wonderful praise announce.[5]

3. Yes, on[6] through life's long path,[7]
   Still singing as you go;
   From youth to age, through night and day,
   In gladness[1] and in sorrow.[8]

4. Still lift your flag high,
   Still march in strong line,
   As soldiers through darkness[9] work
   Until comes[10] golden day.

REFRAIN:

   Rejoice, rejoice, Rejoice, give thanks and sing.

Words, Edward H. Plumptre, 1865.

---

[1] Make the sign for "happy" with one or both hands.
[2] Make the sign for "glory."
[3] Make the sign for "young."
[4] Make the sign for "old."
[5] Make the sign for "tell," if you wish.
[6] Make the sign for "onward" or "forward."
[7] Make the sign for "way" with both "P" hands. Make the sign for "way," if you want.
[8] Make the sign for "sad" or "trouble," if you wish.
[9] Make the sign for "dark."
[10] Make the sign for "sunrise," if you wish.

God, our Father, we love-worship YOU!
We, YOUR children, bless YOUR name!
Chosen in Christ before YOU,
We are "holy without blame."
We love-worship YOU! We love-worship YOU!
Father's praises we announce!
We love-worship YOU! We love-worship YOU!
Father's praises we announce!

Son forever, we love-worship YOU!
Lamb on throne on high!
Lamb from God, we humble before YOU,
YOU have brought YOUR people near!
We love-worship YOU! We love-worship YOU!
Son HIS God, who came die!
We love-worship YOU! We love-worship YOU!
Son HIS God, who came die!

Holy Spirit, we love-worship YOU!
Comforter and heavenly friend!
Sent from God and from Savior,
YOU have led us into rest.
We love-worship YOU! We love-worship YOU!
Through YOUR grace forever blessed:
We love-worship YOU! We love-worship YOU!
Through YOUR grace forever blessed.

Father, Son, and Holy Spirit,
Three in One! we give YOU praise!
For all blessings we get,
Heart and voice to YOU we offer!
We love-worship YOU! We love-worship YOU!
YOU we bless, through never-ending days!
We love-worship YOU! We love-worship YOU!
YOU we bless, through never-ending days. Amen.

Words, st. 1, 2, 4, George W. Frazer, 1904; st. 3, Alfred S. Loizeaux, 1953.

Baptist, 1975—3   Baptist, 1956—5

4   Come, Thou Fount of Every Blessing

1. Come, YOU Giver of[1] every blessing,
   Make my heart sing YOUR grace;
   YOUR many[2] mercies, never stopping,
   Require for songs with loudest praise:
   Teach me some sweet song,
   Sung through[3] beautiful voices above;
   Praise mountain! I am standing on that,
   Mountain of YOUR redeeming[4] love.

2. Here I establish my altar;[5]
   Here through YOUR help I have come;
   And I hope, through YOUR good pleasure,
   Safely arrive at home:
   Jesus sought[6] me when stranger,
   Straying from fence HIS God;
   HE, save me from danger,
   Gave HIS sweet-important blood.

3. O to grace truly great debtor
   Daily I am feeling[7] become!
   Let YOUR grace now,[8] like chain,
   Join my straying heart to YOU:
   Easy stray, Lord, I feel it,
   Easy leave God I love;
   Here is my heart, O take and keep heart,
   Keep heart for YOUR presence above.

Words, Robert Robinson, 1758.

[1] "Of" may be omitted.
[2] Use "stream (river) full mercy" rather than "YOUR many mercies," if you prefer.
[3] Make a sign for "with" instead of "through," if you like.
[4] Make the sign for "save" or "salvation." You can make a sign for "save" with both "R" hands
[5] Place both "A" hands together, thumbs touching and palms facing down. Now move both hand
   away from each other horizontally and then vertically with both palms facing each other.
[6] Make the sign for "seek" or "look."
[7] You may make a sign for "forced," if you like.
[8] "Goodness" is used in other hymnals. You may use either "goodness" or "grace now."

. We praise YOU, O God, our Redeemer,[1] Maker,
In thankful worship our honor[2] we bring.
We put honor before[3] YOU, we kneel and love-worship YOU,
We bless YOUR holy name, happy praises we sing.

. We worship YOU, God of our fathers, we bless YOU;
Through life's sorrow and trouble our Leader YOU are.[4]
When dangers come near us, YOU will not leave us,
And with YOUR help, O God, our wars we win.

. With voices[5] united[6] our praises we offer,
To YOU, wonderful God, happy songs we offer.
YOUR strong arm will lead us, our God is near us,
To YOU, our wonderful Redeemer, forever be[7] praise. Amen.

Words, Julia Cady Cory, 1902.

Make the sign for "Savior" with both "R" hands.
Make the sign for "gift," if you wish.
Make the sign for "presence" or "in front."
Make the sign for "true" or "truly."
Make the sign for "hands," if you want.
Make the sign for "cooperate," if you want.
Make the sign for "give" instead of "be," if you wish.

Baptist, 1975—15   Baptist, 1956—11

Doxology   6

Praise God, from whom all blessings flow;
Praise HIM, all people here on earth;
Praise HIM above, you heavenly group;[1]
Praise Father, Son, and Holy Spirit. Amen.

Words, Thomas Ken, 1695.

[1] Make the sign for "class."

Baptist, 1975—6   Baptist, 1956—514   Broadman—481

1. O come, loud songs let us sing,
   Loud thanks to our All-powerful King;
   For we our voices[1] high should offer,
   When our salvation's Maker[2] we praise.

2. Into HIS presence let us hurry,
   Thank HIM for HIS kindness[3] past;
   To HIM tell, in happy songs,
   Praise that to HIS name belongs.[4]

3. Deep earth is in HIS hand,
   Earth's secret riches at HIS order;
   Strong hills that reach sky,
   Under HIS kingdom shows.

4. O let us to HIS presence go,
   And humble ourselves with worship;
   On our knees, respecting[5]
   Before[6] Lord, our Maker, kneel.

Words, Tate and Brady's *New Version,* 1696.

---

[1] Make the sign for "hands," if you prefer.
[2] Make the sign for "Giver" or "Rock."
[3] Make the sign for "kind."
[4] Make the sign for "join."
[5] Make the sign for "worship" instead of "respect," if you wish.
[6] Make the sign for "presence" or "in front."

Baptist, 1975—21

Glory be[1] to Father, and to Son, and to Holy Spirit;
As it was in beginning, is now, and always shall be,
World without end. Amen, Amen.

Words, Anonymous, 4th Century.

---

[1] Make the sign for "true" or "truly."

Baptist, 1975—4	Baptist, 1956—524	Broadman—494
5	525	495
	526	496

Praise Him, O Praise Him   9

1. Praise HIM, O praise HIM,
   Praise Lord for all HIS blessings;
   Praise HIM, O praise HIM,
   Sing happy song before[1] HIM;
   Praise HIM, O praise HIM,
   Sing happy, victorious[2] song.

2. Glory and honor,
   Glory give to God Father;
   Glory and honor
   To Son and Holy Spirit;
   Praise HIM, O praise HIM,
   Sing happy, victorious song. Amen.

Words, Mary Lou Reynolds, 1970. © Copyright 1970 Broadman Press. All rights reserved.

---

[1] Make the sign for "presence" or "in front."
[2] Make the sign for "victory" or "celebrate."

Baptist, 1975—18

Come, Thou Almighty King

1. Come, God all powerful[1] King, Help us YOUR name sing,
   Help us praise: Father! all glory, over all winning,
   Come and control over us, God eternal.[2]

2. Come, Jesus, God in body, with YOUR powerful Word,
   Our prayer hear! Come, and YOUR people bless,
   And give YOUR Word success: Holy Spirit, on us come.

3. Come, Holy Spirit Comforter, YOUR holy witness give,
   During now happy hour! God truly all powerful,
   Now control every heart, And never from us leave, powerful Spirit.

4. To YOU, wonderful One in Three Person, Person, Person,[3]
   Highest praises give, From now on; HIS kind majesty[4]
   Let us in glory see, And during eternity[2] love and worship. Amen.

Words, Anonymous.

[1] Make the sign for "power."
[2] Make the sign for "forever." If you wish, sign "forever" with the right "E" hand.
[3] Make the sign for "person" three times—one to the left, one in the middle, and one to the right
[4] Make the sign for "glory" with the right "M" hand, the palm facing downward. If you wish, you can just sign "glory."

Baptist, 1975—2   Baptist, 1956—12   Broadman—

1. O worship King, all glory above
   And thankfully sing HIS wonderful love;
   Our Help and Protection, God Eternal,[1]
   Lived in heavenly glory, and full with praise.

2. O tell about HIS power, O sing about HIS grace,
   Whose life is[2] light, whose blue heaven!
   HIS chariot showing anger[3] black thunderclouds make,
   And dark is HIS path[4] on wing of[5] storm.

3. YOUR plentiful care what language[6] can say?
   That breathes in air, that shines in light,
   That flows from hills, that flows to flatland,
   And sweetly drops in wetness and rain.

4. Weak children of earth, and weak as not strong,
   In YOU really we trust, not find YOU fail:
   YOUR mercies really soft, really strong to end,
   Our Maker, Protector, Redeemer,[7] and Friend. Amen.

Words, Robert Grant, 1833.

Make the sign for "forever." You may make a sign for "forever" with the right "E" hand.
Make the sign for "truly."
Make the sign for "angry" or "mad."
Make the sign for "way." You may make a sign for "way" with both "P" hands.
Omit "on wing of" and just sign "way through storm," if you prefer.
Use "word" in place of "language," if you desire.
Make the sign for "Savior." You may make a sign for "Savior" with both "R" hands.

1. Jesus, lover of my soul, Let me to YOUR breast[1] fly,
While nearer waters roll, While storm still is high:[2]
Hide me, O my Savior, hide, Until storm of life is past,
Safe into heaven; O receive my soul at last.[3]

2. Other protection have I none; Depends my helpless[4] soul on YOU:
Leave, O leave me not alone, Still support and comfort me:
All my trust on YOU is made,[5] All my help from YOU I bring;
Cover my defenseless[6] head With black shape of YOUR wing.

3. YOU, O Christ, are all I want, More than all in YOU I find:
Raise[7] fallen,[8] cheer[9] weak, Heal sick, and lead blind:
Right and holy is YOUR name, I am all not righteousness;[10]
False and full with sin I am, YOU are full with truth and grace.

4. Plenteous[11] grace with YOU is found, Grace cover all my sin;
Let healing water flow; Make and keep me pure within:
YOU giving life water are, Freely let me take from YOU;
Overflow[12] YOU within my heart, Rise to all forever.

Words, Charles Wesley, 1738.

---

[1] Make the sign for "chest."
[2] Make the sign for "awful" or "blow," if you want.
[3] Make the sign for "final," if you want.
[4] Make the sign for "help" to be followed with outspread hands.
[5] Make the sign for "decide" or "stay," if you want.
[6] Make the sign for "protect" to be followed with outspread hands.
[7] Make the sign for "help," if you wish.
[8] Make the sign for "fall" or "falling." Add the sign for "people," if you want, such as "fallin people," "weak people," "sick people," and "blind people."
[9] Make the signs for "make happy" if you don't know the sign for "cheer."
[10] Make the sign for right by moving the right "R" hand, palm facing left, forward across the left open, upward palm. Make the sign for "right doing," if you want.
[11] Make the sign for "plenty."
[12] Make the sign for "runneth over." Move the right hand up and over the left "C" hand, both palms facing each other.

Baptist, 1975—172   Baptist, 1956—156   Broadman—172
157   173
158

1. All praise power HIS Jesus' name!
   Let angels kneel;
   Bring that royal[1] crown,
   And crown HIM Lord over all;
   Bring that royal crown,
   And crown HIM Lord over all.

2. You chosen people from Jewish race,[2]
   You saved from sin,
   Praise HIM who saves you through HIS grace,
   And crown HIM Lord over all;
   Praise HIM who saves you through HIS grace,
   And crown HIM Lord over all.

3. Let each family, each race,
   On this earth,
   To HIM all majesty[3] give,
   And crown HIM Lord over all;
   To HIM all majesty give,
   And crown HIM Lord over all.

4. O then with there holy group[4]
   We before[5] Jesus kneel!
   We will join that everlasting[6] song,
   And crown HIM Lord over all;
   We will join that everlasting song,
   And crown HIM Lord over all. Amen.

Words, st. 1, 2, Edward Perronet, 1779; st. 3, 4, John Rippon, 1787.

Make the sign for "king." If you like, you may make the sign for "king" with the right "R" hand, palm facing self.
Make the sign for "family" with both "R" hands. You may sign just "group" or "class."
Make the sign for "glory" with the right "M" hand, palm facing downward.
Make the sign for "class."
Make the sign for "presence."
Make the sign for "forever."

Baptist, 1975—40   Baptist, 1956—132   Broadman—255
              41   133   256
              42   134

1. Strong protector[1] is our God,
   Protection never failing;
   Our Helper He, among people's
   Much troubles succeeding:
   Because still our old enemy
   Really seek give us trouble;
   Enemy's cleverness[2] and power are great,
   And, has awful hate,
   On earth there none equal enemy.

2. We in our strength depend,
   Our trying will really fail;
   If not for right Man on our side,
   Man that God chose:
   Ask who that Man is?
   Christ Jesus, that is HE,
   Lord HIS armies,[3] HIS name,
   From year to year same,
   And HE must win war.

3. And no matter this world, with devils filled,
   Should try hurt us,
   We will not fear, because God has[4] decided
   HIS truth win through us:
   Prince from Darkness[5] awful—
   We fear not for him;[6]
   His anger we can stand,
   Because, look, his ruin is sure,
   One small word shall kill him.

4. That word above all earthly rulers,[7]
   No thanks to rulers, continue;
   Spirit and gifts are ours
   Through HIM who with us support:
   Let things and people go,
   This earthly life, too;
   Body people can kill:
   God's truth continues,
   HIS kingdom is forever. Amen.

Words, Martin Luther, 1529; translated, Frederick H. Hedge, 1853.

Make the sign for "protect" or "defend," ending with the sign for "er" as in "teacher" when using "protector." Just sign "protect" when using "protection."
Make the sign for "clever." If you don't know the sign for "clever," make the sign for "smart" or "skill."
Make the sign for "heavenly armies," "host," or "heavenly hosts."
Make the sign for "finish."
Make the sign for "dark."
Sign "devil" in place of "him," if you prefer.
Make the sign for "control," ending with the sign for "er" as in "teacher."

Baptist, 1975—37   Baptist, 1956—40   Broadman—38

New Born Again   15

1. I found free grace and true love, I am[1] new born again,
   Been long time talking about my troubles here on earth.[2]
   Free grace, free grace, free grace, sinner,
   Free grace, free grace, I am new born again.
   Truly happy, truly happy, I am new born again,
   Been long time talking about my troubles here on earth.

2. I know my Lord has[3] made me free, I am new born again,
   Been long time talking about my troubles here on earth.
   Free grace, free grace, free grace, sinner,
   Free grace, free grace, I am new born again.
   Truly happy, truly happy, I am new born again,
   Been long time talking about my troubles here on earth.

Words, Negro Spiritual.

[1] Make the sign for "truly."
[2] Make the sign for "below" instead of "on earth," if you prefer.
[3] Make the sign for "finish."

Baptist, 1975—474

1. When morning paints[1] sky, My heart waking up shouts,
   Give Jesus Christ praise! Same at work and prayer,
   To Jesus I go; Give Jesus Christ praise.

2. When sweet church bell Rings[2] over hill and valley,
   Give Jesus Christ praise! O listen to what bell sings,
   Same happily bell rings, Give Jesus Christ praise.

3. You nations of people, In your agreement[3] find:
   Give Jesus Christ praise! Let all earth around
   Make joy with noise: Give Jesus Christ praise.

4. In heaven's eternal[4] happiness[5] Pretty song is this,
   Give Jesus Christ praise! Let earth, and sea, and sky
   From deep to high answer, Give Jesus Christ praise. Amen.

Words, *Katholiches Gesangbuch,* Wurzburg, 1828; translated, Edward Caswall, 1854.

---

[1] Make the sign for "bright" or "clear" slowly, as if the sun is starting to give its light that become bright. Sign "paint," if you prefer.

[2] Make the sign for "sound" if you don't know the other sign for "ring," which is sometimes used by the deaf themselves.

[3] Make the sign for "agree." You can make the sign for "cooperate," if you like this one better than "agree."

[4] Make the sign for "forever." You may make the sign for "forever" with the right "E" hand.

[5] Make the sign for "happy."

1. Prettiest Lord Jesus, Ruler[1] over all nature,[2]
O YOU from God and man Son; YOU will I love,
YOU will I honor, YOU, my soul's glory, joy, and crown.

2. Pretty are[3] green growings, Prettier still trees,
Seen in green spread of spring; Jesus is prettiest,
Jesus is purer, WHO makes sad heart sing.

3. Pretty is sunshine, Prettier still moonlight
And all shining starry host;[4] Jesus shines brighter,
Jesus shines purer Than all angels heaven can boast.

4. Beautiful[5] Savior, Lord over all nations,
Son from God and Son from man! Glory and honor,
Praise, worship,[6] Now and forever become YOURS! Amen.

Words, Anonymous German Hymn, *Münster Gesangbuch,* 1677; translated, st. 1-3, Source Unknown, 1850; st. 4, Joseph A. Seiss, 1873.

Make the sign for "control," ending with the sign for "er" as in "teacher."
Make the sign for "world." You can make the sign for "world" with both "N" hands.
Make the sign for "truly."
Make the sign for "class" in front of you at forehead level.
You may make the sign for "wonderful" in place of "beautiful" or "pretty."
You may make the sign for "love-worship" instead of just "worship."

18   We Praise Thee with Our Minds, O Lord

1. We praise YOU with our minds, O Lord,
   Kept[1] thinking clearly YOUR thought;
   Come, Holy Spirit with grace given,
   Teach what Christ has taught.
   In all our learning let us seek
   That wisdom[2] from above
   That comes to all; brave, humble,
   Who ask in faith and love.

2. We praise YOU through our bodies, Lord,
   Kept strong do YOUR want;
   YOUR Spirit's people, who make[3]
   Way for praising YOU still.
   We give ourselves, gift,
   Live as to YOU;
   Because YOU alone have paid price
   Bring salvation free.

3. We praise YOU in our hearts, O King,
   Kept pure know YOUR ways;
   And offer to YOU song sing
   Forever YOUR praise.
   No matter loving hearts will humble
   As year through years roll;
   We praise YOU in our lives now,
   Mind, body, heart, and soul.

Words, Hugh T. McElrath, 1964. © Copyright 1964. Broadman Press. All rights reserved.

[1] You may make the sign for "continue" if you wish.
[2] Make the sign for "wise."
[3] If you wish, make the signs for these words: "YOUR Spirit's bodies, that give."

Baptist, 1975—45

. Praise Lord, King HIS glory,
   Kind Son HIS God is He;
   Long before told[1] through prophets holy,
   Great in power and glory.[2]
   With Father through making,
   Heaven and earth truly tell HIS fame;[3]
   Hope and joy of every nation,
   Life and light are in HIS name.

. Blessed be Lord HIS glory,
   Person with rightness[4] and grace;
   Sing, O earth, wonderful story;
   Jesus redeems[5] sinning people,
   Praise HIM for HIS wonderful salvation,
   Sweet, important Lamb[6] from God love-worship;
   Lord and light of all people,[7]
   Praise and serve HIM forever.

. Strong is King HIS glory,
   HIS wonderful works heavens tell;
   Full of glory and holy,
   Lord HIS armies HIS name!
   Many nations[8] in happy group[9]
   Sing HIS praise with sweetest sound;[10]
   In our hearts HE controls over us,
   King of kings and Lord of lords!

ords, Delma B. Reno, 1964. © Copyright 1964 Broadman Press. All rights reserved.

Make the sign for "predict," "prophecy," or "vision" if you know it.
If you prefer, make the sign for "glory" with the right "M" hand, the palm facing downward, when using "majesty."
Make the sign for "famous."
Make the sign for "right." You may make the signs for "sun of righteousness" if you wish to use the abstract phrase instead of "person with rightness."
Make the sign for "save" with both "R" hands.
"Lamb of God" is one of many names for Jesus; you may use "Son of God."
You may make the sign for "making" when using "creation."
Make the signs for "many languages" when using "myriad tongues" if you wish.
Make the sign for "class" or "host."
Make the sign for "music" instead of "sound" if you prefer.

1. God be[1] with you until we meet again!
   Through advices guide, keep you,
   With HIS sheep[2] safely wrap[3] you;
   God be with you until we meet again!

2. God be with you until we meet again!
   Under HIS wings safely hide you,
   Daily bread still give you;
   God be with you until we meet again! Amen.

Words, Jeremiah E. Rankin, 1880.

---

[1] Make the sign for "truly" or "true."
[2] Make the sign for "people" instead of "sheep," if you want.
[3] Make the sign for "around."

Baptist, 1975—261   **Baptist, 1956—372**   **Broadman—48**

21   For the Beauty of the Earth

1. For the beauty of earth,
   For glory of sky,
   For love which from our birth
   Over and around us there:
   Christ our God, to YOU we offer
   This our song with thankful praise.

2. For wonder[1] of[2] hour
   Of day and of night,
   Hill and valley and tree and flower,
   Sun and moon, and stars giving light:
   Christ our God, to YOU we offer
   This our song with thankful praise.

For joy[3] of people's love,
Brother, sister, parent, child,
Friends on earth, and friends above,
For all kind thoughts and sweet;
Christ our God, to YOU we offer
This our song with thankful praise.

For YOUR church that always
Lift holy hands above,
Offering on every shore
Church's pure sacrifice[4] showing love;
Christ our God, to YOU we offer
This our song with thankful praise.

For joy of ear and eye,
For heart and mind enjoy,
For wonderful way
Joining feeling to sound and sight;[5]
Christ our God, to YOU we offer
This our song with thankful praise.

For YOURSELF, best Gift Divine![6]
To our world truly freely given;
For that wonderful, wonderful love of YOURS,
Peace on earth, and joy in heaven:
Christ, our God, to YOU we offer
This our song with thankful praise. Amen.

Words, Folliott S. Pierpoint, 1864.

Make the sign for "surprise," "think," or "wonderful."
Make the sign for "during" instead of "of," if you want.
Make the sign for "happy" with one or both hands.
Place both "S" hands, palms facing up, in front of you. Move both hands upward while changing them into the sign for "offer."
Make the sign for "eyes."
Make the sign for "holy" with the right "D" hand, palm facing down.

1. O I want one thousand languages for singing,
   Blessed be name HIS Lord!
   Glory about my God and King,
   Blessed be name HIS Lord!

2. Jesus, that name quiets my fears,
   Blessed be name HIS Lord!
   This music[1] in sinner's ears,
   Blessed be name HIS Lord!

3. He breaks power-canceled[2] sin,
   Blessed be name HIS Lord!
   HIS blood can make worst sinner clean,
   Blessed be name HIS Lord!

4. I never shall forget that day,
   Blessed be name HIS Lord!
   When Jesus washed my sins away.
   Blessed be name HIS Lord!

REFRAIN:

   Blessed be name, Blessed be name,
   Blessed be name HIS Lord!
   Blessed be name, Blessed be name,
   Blessed be name HIS Lord!

Words, Charles Wesley, 1739, alt.; Refrain, Ralph E. Hudson, 1887.

---

[1] Make a sign for "song" with right "M" hand, the palm facing downward.
[2] Make a sign for "abolish," "take away," or "remove," in place of "canceled."

Have you failed in your plan for your troubled life?
Put your hand in HIS nailed[1] hand;
Are you tired and weak from life's work and trouble?[2]
Put your hand in HIS nailed hand.

Are you walking alone through shadow of death?[3]
Put your hand in HIS nailed hand;
Christ will comfort your heart, put your trust in HIM,
Put your hand in HIS nailed hand.

Will[4] you follow want HIS risen Lord?
Put your hand in HIS nailed hand;
Will you live in light[5] of HIS wonderful Word?
Put your hand in HIS nailed hand.

Is your soul burdened with heavy sin?
Put your hand in HIS nailed hand;
Open your heart wide, let Savior in,
Put your hand in HIS nailed hand.

REFRAIN:

Put your hand in HIS nailed hand,
Put your hand in HIS nailed hand;
HE will keep to end, HE is your loving friend,
Put your hand in HIS nailed hand.

ords, B. B. McKinney, 1924. Copyright 1924. Renewal 1952 Broadman Press. All rights reserved.

---

ouch the left open palm with the fingertip of the right hand. Then, hit the left open palm with
e right "S" hand, the edge of the little finger touching and the palm facing left or the left
houlder.
ake a sign for "fighting" instead of "trouble," if you prefer.
ake the sign for "black shape" as in Psalm 23, "valley of the shadow of death."
ake the sign for "want" instead of "will," if you prefer.
gn "understanding," if you like this better.

1. Crown Jesus with many crowns,
   Lamb on HIS throne;
   Listen! how heavenly music continues
   More beautiful above all music:
   Awake, my soul, and sing
   About HIM who died for me,
   And welcome HIM as my highest King
   Through all eternity.

2. Crown HIM Lord over life,
   Who victoriously overcame grave,
   And rose victorious in war with devil
   For people HE came save;
   HIS glory now we sing
   Who died, and rose above,
   Who died eternal life give,
   And lives that death will finish.

3. Crown HIM Lord of peace,
   Whose power controls kings
   From north to south, that wars will stop,
   And all becomes prayer and praise:
   HIS control will never end,
   And around HIS nailed feet
   Beautiful flowers of heaven give
   Their smell always sweet.

4. Crown HIM Lord of love;
   Look at HIS hands and side,
   Those hands and side still can see above,
   In beauty made glorious:
   All welcome, Redeemer, welcome!
   Because YOU have died for me:
   YOUR praise and glory will not fail
   During all eternity. Amen.

Words, st. 1, 3, 4, Matthew Bridges, 1851; st. 2, Godfrey Thring, 1874.

Baptist, 1975—52   Baptist, 1956—152   Broadman—

Wonderful Redeemer, we love-worship YOU,
God HIS mercy, love, and grace;
Warm our hearts with YOUR presence,
Let us see YOUR kind face!
Wonderful Redeemer, we love-worship YOU,
God's wonderful love to people YOU are:
We love-worship YOU, Wonderful Redeemer,
Control highest in every heart.

Wonderful Redeemer, we ask YOU,
Take our doubts and fears away;
Let YOUR face smile on us,
Shine on us YOUR light today!
Wonderful Redeemer, we love-worship YOU,
Highest hills announce YOUR fame;
We love-worship YOU, Wonderful Redeemer,
People and angels praise YOUR name.

Life and love from YOU are shining,
Sin and sorrow melt;
King kindness, God HIS glory,
Fill us with YOURSELF today!
Wonderful Redeemer, we love-worship YOU,
Life and freedom are YOURS;
We love-worship YOU, Wonderful Redeemer,
Fill us with YOUR love divine.

When we see YOU in YOUR beauty,
As YOU are, then we will become;
Like YOURSELF YOU have made us,
Wonderful Redeemer, we love YOU!
Wonderful Redeemer, we love-worship YOU,
Like YOU we will become;
We love-worship YOU, Wonderful Redeemer,
God HIS life eternally. Amen.

ords, John Roy Harris, 1934. From *The Broadman Hymnal,* Copyright 1940; Renewal 1968
oadman Press. All rights reserved.

1. "Man with sorrows," wonderful name
   Because Son from God who came
   Ruined sinners save!
   Hallelujah![1] Wonderful Savior!

2. Carrying[2] shame and laughing,[3]
   In my place punished HE stood,
   Sealed[4] my pardon with HIS blood;
   Hallelujah! Wonderful Savior!

3. Sinful, dirty, and helpless we,
   Perfect Lamb[5] from God was[6] HE;
   Full salvation![7] can that be?
   Hallelujah! Wonderful Savior!

4. Crucified was HE die,
   "It is finished," was HIS shout,
   Now in heaven exalted[8] high,
   Hallelujah! Wonderful Savior!

5. When HE comes, our glorious[9] King,
   All HIS saved people home bring,
   Then again new this song we will sing,
   Hallelujah! Wonderful Savior!

Words, Philip P. Bliss, 1875.

---

[1] Make a sign for "praise" + "victory." You can make the sign with both hands for "H" + "praise" + "victory," using the basic sign for "victory" without the "V's."

[2] You may make a sign for "accept" if you prefer this one.

[3] Make the sign for "mocking" by using both clenched hands with the index and little finger extended forward.

[4] Make a sign for "branding" or "stamping" by hitting the open left hand with the right "S" hand, palm facing left. Sign "Gave me pardon," if you wish.

[5] "Lamb" is one of the many names for Jesus who died as a lamb for man's sin. You may use "Son" instead of "Lamb."

[6] Make a sign for "truly."

[7] You may make a sign for "forgive(ness)" instead of "salvation."

[8] Make the sign for "lifting" or "raising." You can make the sign for "lifting" with both "E" hands.

[9] Make the sign for "glory."

. Blessed Savior, we love-worship YOU,
We YOUR love and grace announce;[1]
YOU are strong, YOU are holy,
Glorious is YOUR wonderful name!

. Wonderful Redeemer, Lord and Master,[2]
Light over all eternal days;
Let YOUR people from every nation
Sing YOUR right[3] and endless praise!

. From throne full heaven's glory
To cross full sin and shame,
YOU really came die exchange,
Guilty[4] sinners save!

. Come, O come, eternal Savior,
Come and take YOUR royal[5] throne;
Come, and control, and control forever,
Be kingdom all YOURS!

EFRAIN:

Glorious, Glorious, Glorious is YOUR name, O Lord!
Glorious is YOUR name, O Lord! Glorious is YOUR name, O Lord!
Glorious, Glorious, Glorious is YOUR name, O Lord! Amen.

ords, B. B. McKinney, 1942. Copyright 1942, Renewal 1970 Broadman Press. All rights reserved.

Make the sign for "tell."
You may sign "Ruler" if you don't know the sign for "Master."
You may make the sign for "perfect."
Strike the heart area twice with the right "G" hand, palm facing left and slightly downward.
Make the sign for "king." You may make the sign for "king" with the right "R" hand, palm facing elf.

1. Love divine,[1] better than all loves,[2]
   Joy from heaven, to earth come down;
   Make in us YOUR humble living;
   All YOUR faithful[3] mercies crown.
   Jesus, YOU are full mercy,
   Pure, no limited love YOU are;
   Visit us with YOUR salvation;
   Enter every trembling[4] heart.

2. Breathe, O breathe YOUR loving Spirit
   Into every troubled person!
   Let us all in YOU receive,
   Let us find promise rest;
   Take away our want sinning;
   First and last YOU continue;
   End of faith, same faith's beginning,
   Make our hearts free.

3. Come, powerful God, save us,
   Let us all YOUR grace receive;
   Fast coming again, and never,
   Never YOUR peoples leave.
   YOU we will be always blessing,
   Serve YOU same YOUR hosts[5] above,
   Pray, and praise YOU without stopping,
   Glory in YOUR perfect love.

4. Finish, then, YOUR new creation;[6]
   Pure and perfect let us become;
   Let us see YOUR wonderful salvation
   Perfectly found in YOU:
   Changed from glory to glory,
   Until in heaven we accept our place,
   Until we put our crowns before[7] YOU,
   Felt[8] with wonder, love, and praise. Amen.

Words, Charles Wesley, 1743.

---

[1] Make the sign for "holy." You can make the sign for "holy" with the right "D" hand.

sign "all love high" or "all love above" instead of "better than all loves," if you prefer.
Make the sign for "regular" with both "F" hands.
Make both hands as if in fright or nervousness, palms facing self.
Make the sign for "classes" in midair above your line of vision.
Make the sign for "make." Make the sign for "make" with both "C" hands, if you prefer.
Make the sign for "presence."
Make the sign for "full" instead of "felt," if you wish. "Lost" may be signed, but the idea or meaning may not be clear to the deaf worshipers.

O for a Thousand Tongues to Sing   29

O I want one thousand languages for singing
My wonderful Redeemer's[1] praise,
Glory about my God and King,
And victory join with HIS grace!

My kind Master[2] and my God,
Help me announce,[3]
And spread over all earth,
Giving honor to HIS name.

Jesus, that name quiets my fears,
That tells my sorrow stop;
True music[4] for sinners listen;
Giving life, health, and peace.

HE destroys power that controls sinner,
HE makes sinner free;
HIS blood can make awful sinner clean,
HIS blood saved me. Amen.

Words, Charles Wesley, 1739.

Make the sign for "Savior." If you wish, you may make the sign for "Savior" with both "R" hands.
Make the sign for "Lord." You may make the sign for "master," instead.
You may make the sign for "tell."
Make the sign for "song." If you wish, you may make the sign for "song" with the right "M" hand, palm facing downward.

1. I stand surprised in presence HIS
   Jesus from Nazareth,[1]
   And wonder how HE can love me,
   Sinner, punished, not clean.

2. For me there in garden HE prayed,
   "Not MY want but YOURS";
   HE had no tears for HIS sorrow,
   But sweat drops blood for mine.

3. HE took my sins and my sorrows,
   HE made both HIS own;[2]
   HE carried burden to mountain-cross,
   And suffered and died alone.

4. When with saved people in glory
   HIS face I finally shall see,
   That will be my joy[3] through years[4]
   Sing about HIS love for me.

REFRAIN:

How marvelous![5] How wonderful!
And my song shall always be;
How marvelous! How wonderful!
Is my Savior's love for me!

Words, Charles H. Gabriel, 1905.

---

[1] Make the sign for "N" + "town."
[2] Make the sign for "have" with both "O" hands. Leave it out if you wish.
[3] Make the sign for "happy" with one or both hands.
[4] You may make the sign for "forever," if you like.
[5] Start the sign with the "M" hands and then with the sign for "wonderful."

. There is[1] name I love hear,
  I love sing name's importance;
  That seems as music[2] in my ear,
  Sweetest name on earth.

. Name tells me about Savior's love,
  Who died for making me free;
  That tells me about HIS sweet, important blood,
  Sinner's perfect forgiveness.[3]

. Name tells me what my Father has[4]
  Planned for each day,
  And no matter I walk dark way,
  Gives light all way.

. Name tells about Jesus whose loving heart
  Can feel my deepest trouble,
  Who in each sorrow accepts my trouble,
  No other person can do that.

REFRAIN:

  Oh, truly I love Jesus,
  Oh, truly I love Jesus,
  Oh, truly I love Jesus,
  Because HE first loved me.

Words, Frederick Whitfield, 1855.

Make the sign for "truly."
Make the sign for "song" with the right "M" hand, palm facing downward.
Make the sign for "forgive" or "pardon."
Make the sign for "finish."

1. Praise HIM! praise HIM! Jesus, our wonderful Redeemer:
   Sing, O Earth, HIS wonderful love announce:[1]
   Praise HIM! praise HIM! highest angels in glory;
   Strength[2] and honor give to HIS holy name:
   As shepherd, Jesus will protect HIS children;
   In HIS arms HE carries us all day:

2. Praise HIM! praise HIM! Jesus, our wonderful Redeemer:
   For our sins HE suffered and bled[3] and died;
   HE our protection, our hope for eternal salvation,
   Praise HIM! praise HIM! Jesus crucified:
   Announce HIS praises! Jesus who accepted our sorrows,
   Love without limit, wonderful, deep, and power:

3. Praise HIM! praise HIM! Jesus, our wonderful Redeemer:
   Heaven land loud with praises[4] sing:
   Jesus, Savior, controls forever and forever;
   Crown HIM! crown HIM! prophet and priest[5] and king:
   Christ is coming, over world victory,
   Power and glory to Lord belong:[6]

REFRAIN:

Praise HIM! praise HIM! announce about HIS high importance;
Praise HIM! praise HIM! always in happy song.

Words, Fanny J. Crosby, 1869.

---

[1] You may make the sign for " tell."
[2] You may make the sign for "power."
[3] Make the sign for "blood."
[4] You may make the sign for "hosanna" by beginning with both "H" hands and then clappir both hands twice.
[5] Place both "P" hands above the head, and then make the sign for "crown."
[6] Make the sign for "HIS."

Jesus, thinking about YOU
With sweetness[1] fills my soul;
But sweeter YOUR face see,
And in YOUR presence rest.

No voice can sing, no heart can make,
Or memory find
Sweeter word than Jesus' name,
O Savior for people.

O Hope for every sorrowing heart!
O Joy for all humble!
To all who fall, truly kind YOU are![2]
Truly good to all who seek!

But what to all who find?
Look! this, No language[3] or pen can show
Love from Jesus, what that is
None but HIS loving ones know.

ords, Latin Hymn, 12th Century; translated, Edward Caswall, 1849.

---

ake the sign for "sweet."
ake the sign for "truly."
ake the sign for "word" instead of "language," if you like.

1. I love YOU, I love YOU, I love YOU, my Lord;
   I love YOU, my Savior, I love YOU, my God:
   I love YOU, I love YOU, and that YOU really know;
   But how much I love YOU my actions will show.

2. I am[1] happy, I am happy, oh, wonderful story!
   My happiness is forever, I stand on high mountain:
   I look to heaven and want go there,
   With Jesus and angels and people true love.

3. O Jesus, my Savior, with YOU I am happy,
   My life and salvation, my happiness and my rest:
   YOUR name be my story, and YOUR love be my song;
   YOUR grace will inspire[2] both my heart and my lips.

4. Oh, who is same my Savior. HE is King over peace;
   HE smiles and HE loves me and helps me sing:
   I will praise HIM, I will praise HIM with song very clear,
   While much pleasure my spirit will give happiness.

Words, Anonymous; Jeremiah Ingall's *Christian Harmony,* 1805.

---

[1] Make the sign for "truly."
[2] Place both flattened "O" hands on the chest. Then spread both hands upward, palms fac
self.

Baptist, 1975—75   **Baptist, 1956—150**

My Jesus, I love YOU, I know YOU are[1] mine,
For YOU all my sins I surrender;[2]
My kind Redeemer, my Savior are YOU;
If any time I loved YOU, my Jesus, truly now.

I love YOU because YOU first loved me,
And bought my forgiveness[3] on mountain-cross;
I love YOU for wearing thorns on YOUR forehead;
If any time I loved YOU, my Jesus, truly now.

In heavenly homes full glory and always happiness[4]
I will always worship YOU in heaven truly bright;
I will sing with shining crown on my forehead,
If any time I loved YOU, my Jesus, truly now.

ords, William R. Featherston, c. 1862.

---

ake the sign for "truly."
ake the sign for "give up."
ake the sign for "forgive" or "pardon."
ake the sign for "happy" with one or both hands.

1. O small town name Bethlehem,[1]
   Truly quiet we see town there!
   Over your dark town
   Quiet stars shine;
   Still in your dark streets shines
   Everlasting[2] Light;
   Hopes and fears since many years
   Are[3] meet in Bethlehem tonight.

2. Because Jesus is[3] born from Mary,
   And meeting together above,
   While people sleep, angels continue
   Their watch with wondering love.
   O Morning Star, together,
   Announce[4] Jesus' holy birth,
   And praises sing to God our King,
   And peace to all people on earth!

3. Truly quiet, truly quiet
   This wonderful Gift, Jesus, God gives!
   Truly God gives to people's hearts
   Many blessings from HIS heaven.
   No person can hear Jesus' coming,
   But in here world full sin,
   If humble souls accept Jesus,
   Our loving Jesus enters heart now.

4. O holy Baby from Bethlehem!
   Come to us, we pray;
   Forgive our sin, and enter our hearts,
   Born in us today!
   We hear Christmas angels,
   Wonderful happy story announce;
   O come to us, live continue with us,
   Our Lord God with us.

Words, Phillips Brooks, 1868.

---

[1] Make the sign for "B" + "town."

Make the sign for "forever."
Make the sign for "truly."
You may make the sign for " tell."

Baptist, 1975—85   Baptist, 1956—75   Broadman—144

O Come, All Ye Faithful   37

1. O come, all you faithful[1] people, with joy and victory,
   O come you, O come you to Bethlehem:[2]
   Come, see Jesus, born King over angels!

2. Sing, choir[3] angels, sing with happy praise,
   O sing, all glory group[4] in heaven above!
   Glory to God, all glory in highest:

3. Yes, Lord, we honor-welcome YOU, born that happy morning,
   Jesus, to YOU we give all glory;
   Son from God, finish in body born.

REFRAIN:

   O come, let us love-worship HIM,
   O come, let us love-worship HIM,
   O come, let us love-worship HIM,
   Christ our Lord!

Words, Latin Hymn; ascribed to John Francis Wade, c. 1743; translated, Frederick Oakeley, 1841, and others.

Make the sign for "regular" with both "F" hands.
Make the sign for "B" + "town."
Make the sign for "song" with the right "C" hand, palm facing down.
Make the sign for "class."

Baptist, 1975—81   Baptist, 1956—66   Broadman—143

1. Listen! heavenly[1] angels sing,
    "Glory to newborn King;
    Peace on earth, and mercy sweet;[2]
    God and sinners become friends."
    Joyful,[3] all you nations, rise,[4]
    Join victory host[5] from skies;
    With angelic[6] hosts announce,
    "Christ is born in Bethlehem."[7]
    Listen! heavenly angels sing,
    "Glory to newborn King."

2. Christ, through highest heaven love-worshiped,
    Christ, forever[8] Lord:
    Late in time, watch HIM come,
    Son born from pure mother.
    Lived in body God HIMSELF see,
    Honor-welcome God in body!
    Pleased as man with people live,
    Jesus our God with us.
    Listen! heavenly angels sing,
    "Glory to newborn King."

3. Honor-welcome heaven born Prince of Peace!
    Honor-welcome Sun join with righteousness![9]
    Light and life to all HE brings,
    Risen with healing in HIS wings.
    Sweetly HE leaves HIS glory above,
    Born that man no more may die,
    Born raise sons[10] from earth,
    Born give them second birth.
    Listen! heavenly angels sing,
    "Glory to newborn King."

Words, Charles Wesley, 1739, alt.

---

[1] Make the sign for "serving" or "working" in place of "heavenly," if you like.
[2] Make the sign for "soft" or "kind," if you like either one better than "sweet."
[3] Make the sign for "happy" with one or both hands.
[4] You may make the sign for "stand" in place of "rise."
[5] Make the sign for "class" at eye or forehead level.
[6] Make the sign for "angel."
[7] Make the sign for "B" + "town."

You may make the sign for "everlasting" by moving the right "E" hand in a clockwise circle and then the right "Y" hand forward, palm facing forward all the time.
Move right "R" hand, palm facing left, forward across the left open upward palm. Make the sign for "right-doing," if you prefer.
Make the sign for "children" instead of "sons," if you want.

Away in a Manger   39

Away in manger,[1] no place for bed,
Little Lord Jesus laid down HIS sweet head;
Stars in sky looked down where HE lay,
Little Lord Jesus, asleep on hay.

Cows are[2] mooing,[3] Baby awakes,
But little Lord Jesus, no crying HE makes;
I love YOU, Lord Jesus! look down from sky,
And stay near my bed until morning comes.

Be near me, Lord Jesus, I ask YOU stay
Near me, forever, and love me I pray;
Bless all loving children in YOUR sweet[4] care,
And prepare us for heaven live with YOU there. Amen.

Words, st. 1, 2, Anonymous, 1885; st. 3, Anonymous, 1892.

Make the sign for "feed box."
Make the sign for "true" or "truly."
Make the signs for "Cows say moo" or "Cows truly moo."
Make the sign for "kind" instead of "sweet," if you want.

1. That came on midnight clear,
   That glorious[1] song ago,[2]
   From angels coming near earth,
   Touch harps gold:
   "Peace on earth, good feeling to people,"
   From heaven's kind King.
   World[3] in real quietness[4] lay,
   Hear angels sing.

2. Still with troubles of sin and fighting
   World has[5] suffered long,
   Under angel song have rolled[6]
   Two thousand years of wrong;
   And man, at war with man, hears not
   Love song that angels bring:
   O quiet noise, you men still fighting,
   And hear angels sing.

3. And[7] you, under life's heavy burden,
   Whose bodies are bent low,
   Who work along climbing way
   With hurtful steps and slow,
   Look now! for happy and gold hours
   Come fast on wing:
   O rest near tired road,
   And hear angels sing!

4. For look! days are hurrying on,[8]
   Through prophet song writer before told,
   When with many years
   Comes now year gold;
   When peace shall over all earth
   Peace's old brightness[9] give,
   And all world give again song
   Which now angels sing.

Words, Edmund H. Sears, 1849.

---

[1] Make the sign for "glory."
[2] Make the sign for "long ago" or "old," if you prefer.

Make the sign for "people," if you wish.
Make the sign for "quiet."
Make the sign for "finish."
Make the sign for "come" instead of "rolled," if you prefer.
Make the sign for "all."
Make the sign for "onward" or "forward."
Make the sign for "bright."

Baptist, 1975—86   Baptist, 1956—71   Broadman—141

Good Christian Men, Rejoice   41

1. Good Christian men,[1] rejoice[2] With heart and soul and voice![3]
Give attention to what we say: Jesus Christ is born today.
Man and animal before HIM humble, And HE is in manger[4] now:
Christ is born today, Christ is born today!

2. Good Christian men, rejoice With heart and soul and voice!
Now you hear about forever joy:[5] Jesus Christ was born for this.
HE has opened heaven's door, And man is blessed forever.
Christ was born for this, Christ was born for this!

3. Good Christian men, rejoice With heart and soul and voice!
Now you must not fear death: Jesus was born for saving;
Calls you one, and calls you all, Giving you HIS everlasting[6] home.
Christ was born save (you), Christ was born save (you)!

Words, Medieval Latin Carol, 14th Century; translated, John Mason Neale, 1853.

Make the sign for "people," if you want.
Make the sign for "happy."
Make the sign for "hands" instead of "voice," if you prefer.
"Manger" is a box in which hay is put for horses or cows to eat. Make the sign for "boat,"
but don't rock or shake the hands. Then, move both hands upward and away from each other
as if making the sign for "manger." Make the sign for "feed box," if you want.
Make the sign for "happy" with one or both hands.
Move the right "E" hand in clockwise circle. Then, change the right hand from "E" to "Y," moving
it forward, palm always facing forward. Make sign for "forever," if you prefer it to "everlasting."

Baptist, 1975—90   Baptist, 1956—74

42   Angels, from the Realms of Glory

1. Angels, from kingdom of glory,
   Wing your way over all earth;
   You who sang creation's[1] story,
   Now announce[2] Savior's birth:
   Come and worship, come and worship,
   Worship Christ, newborn King!

2. Shepherds, in fields live continuing,
   Watch over your sheep through night,
   God with man is now living,
   There shines baby Light:
   Come and worship, come and worship,
   Worship Christ, newborn King!

3. Wise men, leave your thoughts,
   Bright dreams shine far;
   Seek wonderful Want of nations,
   You have seen baby star:
   Come and worship, come and worship,
   Worship Christ, newborn King!

4. Christians, before altar[3] kneeling,
   Watching long in hope and fear,
   Suddenly[4] Lord coming down,
   In HIS temple[5] shall appear:
   Come and worship, come and worship,
   Worship Christ, newborn King!

Words, James Montgomery, 1816.

---

[1] Make the sign for "make."
[2] Make the sign for "tell," if you want.
[3] Touch the thumbs of both "A" hands, palms facing downward. Move both hands away from each other. Then bring both "A" hands, palms facing each other, downward.
[4] Make the sign for "fast."
[5] Make the sign for "church," if you want.

Joy to world! Lord has[1] come;
Let earth accept her King;
Let every heart plan Jesus room,
And heaven and nature[2] sing,
And heaven and nature sing,
And heaven, and heaven and nature sing.

Joy to earth! Our Savior controls;
Let people sing continue;
While field and flood, rock, hill, and flat land
Answer again that happy song,
Answer again that happy song,
Answer again, yes, answer again that happy song.

Don't let sin and sorrow grow,
Don't let sin continue spread;
Jesus comes for making HIS blessing spread
Where HE finds sin,
Where HE finds sin,
Where, yes, where HE finds sin.

Jesus controls world with truth and grace,
And makes all nation prove show
Glory join with HIS righteousness,[3]
And wonderful things about HIS love,
And wonderful things about HIS love,
And wonderful, wonderful things about HIS love.

Words, Isaac Watts, 1719.

Make the sign for "finish."
Make the sign for "world." If you wish, you may make the sign for "world" with both "N" hands.
Make the sign for "right" by moving the right "R" hand, palm facing left, across the left flat upward palm.

1. Quiet night, holy night,
   All is quiet, all is bright
   Around there pure mother and baby!
   Holy baby true soft and sweet,
   Sleep in heavenly peace,
   Sleep in heavenly peace.

2. Quiet night, holy night,
   Darkness[1] disappears,[2] all becomes bright;
   Shepherds hear angels sing,
   Praise God! Welcome King!
   Christ Savior is born,
   Christ Savior is born.

3. Quiet night, holy night,
   Son from God, love's pure light;
   Glory shines from Jesus' holy face,
   With coming redeeming[3] grace,
   Jesus, Lord, during YOUR birth,
   Jesus, Lord, during YOUR birth.

4. Quiet night, holy night,
   Wonderful Star, give YOUR light;
   With angels, let us sing,
   Praise to our King;
   Christ Savior is born,
   Christ Savior is born.

Words, German Hymn, Joseph Mohr. Translated, st. 1, 3, John Freeman Young, 1863; st. 4, Anonymous.

---

[1] Make the sign for "dark."
[2] Make the sign for "melt."
[3] Make the sign for "saving." If you want, you may make the sign for "saving" with both "R hands.

1. First Christmas song angel really say,
   Was to some poor shepherds in fields where shepherds lay;
   In fields where they lay keeping their sheep,
   On cold winter's night that was very dark.

2. For all see there was star
   Shining in east above shepherds far,
   And to earth star gave great light,
   And truly star continued both day and night.

3. And through light from that same star
   Wise Men came from country far;
   Seek for King was their purpose,
   And follow star where star went.[1]

4. Then let us all with one agreement[2]
   Sing praises to our heavenly Lord
   Who had made heaven and earth from nothing,
   And with HIS blood people has bought.

REFRAIN:

   Christmas song, Christmas song,
   Christmas song, Christmas song,
   Born is King of Israel.[3]

Words, Traditional English Carol.

---

[1] Make the sign for "lead" or "led," if you wish.
[2] Make the sign for "agree" or "cooperate."
[3] Make the sign for "Jews" if you don't know the sign for "Israel."

Baptist, 1975—91   Baptist, 1956—63   Broadman—140

1. While shepherds watched their sheep through night,
   All seated on ground,
   Angel HIS Lord came down,
   And glory shone around.

2. "Fear not!" said angel; because awful fear
   Had filled their[1] troubled minds,
   "Happy news with great joy I bring,
   To you and all people.

3. "To you, in David's[2] town, today
   Is born from David's family,
   Savior who is Christ Lord;
   And this shall be show.[3]

4. "Heavenly Baby you there shall find
   To people's eyes shown,
   All softly wrapped in clothing,
   And in manger[4] laid."

5. This[5] said angel, and suddenly[6]
   Appeared shining host[7]
   Of angels praising God, who in this way
   Sang their happy song:

6. "All glory be to God on high,
   And to earth be peace:
   Kind feeling now on[8] from heaven to men.[9]
   Begin and never stop!"

Words, paraphrased, Nahum Tate, 1700.

---

[1] Make the sign for "shepherds," if you want.
[2] Make the sign for "king" with the right "D" hand, palm facing self.
[3] Make the sign for "proof," if you like it better than "show."
[4] Make the sign for "feed box."
[5] The word "thus" really means "therefore." For the sake of brevity, "this" is given.
[6] Make the sign for "fast."
[7] Make the sign for "class" at the eye or forehead level.
[8] Place the left open hand, palm facing self, near the chest area. Touch the back of the left hand

with the right open palm. Move the right hand forward.
Make the sign for "people," if you want to use it rather than "men."

Were You There?   47

1. Were[1] you there when soldiers crucified[2] my Lord?
   Were you there when soldiers crucified my Lord?
   Oh! Sometimes that makes me tremble,[3] tremble, tremble.
   Were you there when soldiers crucified my Lord?

2. Were you there when soldiers nailed HIM to cross?
   Were you there when soldiers nailed HIM to cross?
   Oh! Sometimes that makes me tremble, tremble, tremble.
   Were you there when soldiers nailed HIM to cross?

3. Were you there when people buried HIM in grave?
   Were you there when people buried HIM in grave?
   Oh! Sometimes that makes me tremble, tremble, tremble.
   Were you there when people buried HIM in grave?

Words, Traditional Negro Spiritual; adapted, John W. Work, Jr., and Frederick J. Work, 1907.

Make the sign for "true" or "truly."
Hit the left open palm with the right "S" hand, palm facing left; then, the right open palm with the left "S" hand, palm facing right. Spread out both arms as if they are hung on a cross.
Make the sign for "tremble" by shaking both hands, palms toward you. Shake the hands as if you are scared or afraid.

1. Angels we have heard on high,
   Sweetly singing over land:
   And mountains in answer,
   Give their joyful[1] songs.

2. Shepherds, why this happy song?
   Why your joyful noise continue?
   What happy news be[2]
   That inspires[3] your heavenly song?

3. Come to Bethlehem,[4] and see
   HIM whose birth angels sing;
   Come, love-worship on bended knee
   Christ Lord, newborn King.

4. See HIM in manger[5] laid,
   Whom choirs[6] angels praise;
   Mary, Joseph, give your help,
   While our hearts in love we offer.

REFRAIN:

     Glory in highest to God!
     Glory in highest to God!

Words, Traditional French Carol; translated, Source Unknown, 1862, alt.

---

[1] Make the sign for "happy" with one or both hands.
[2] Make the sign for "true" or "truly."
[3] Touch the chest area with both flattened "O" hands. Then spread both hands upward. Make the sign for "make," if you wish.
[4] Make the sign for "B" with the right hand, ending with the sign for "town."
[5] Make the sign for "feed box."
[6] Make the sign for "song" with the right "C" hand, palm facing down. Make the sign for "class" at the eye or forehead level in front of self.

Baptist, 1975—95   Baptist, 1956—64

. O sing song about Bethlehem,[1]
About shepherds watching there,
And about news that came to shepherds
From angels in sky.
Light that shone on Bethlehem
Fills all world today;
About Jesus' birth and peace on earth
Angels sing alway.

. O sing song about Nazareth,[2]
About sun(ny) days full joy,
O sing about sweet smelling flowers
And about never sinning Boy;
Because now flowers in Nazareth
In every heart can grow;
Now spreads fame[3] HIS Jesus' loving name
On all winds that blow.

. O sing song about Galilee,
About water and tree and hill,
About HIM[4] who walked on sea
And made waves become quiet;
Because no matter same waves on Galilee,
Dark sea with trouble roll,
When faith has[5] heard Master's[6] word,
Comes peace on soul.

'ords, Louis F. Benson, 1899.

Make the sign for "B" + "town."
Make the sign for "N" + "town."
Make the sign for "famous."
Make the sign for "Jesus" in place of "HIM," if you prefer.
Make the sign for "finish."
Make the sign for "Savior" if you don't know the sign for "Master."

There Is a Fountain

1. There is fountain[1] filled with blood
   Coming from Savior's body;
   And sinners, cleaned under that blood,
   Lose all their guilty[2] sins:
   Lose all their guilty sins,
   Lose all their guilty sins;
   And sinners, cleaned under that blood,
   Lose all their guilty sins.

2. Dying thief rejoiced see
   That blood in his day;
   And there can I, no matter sinful same he,
   Wash all my sins away:
   Wash all my sins away,
   Wash all my sins away;
   And there can I, no matter sinful same he,
   Wash all my sins away.

3. Loving, dying, Lamb,[3] YOUR sweet, important blood
   Shall never lose power
   Until all saved church HIS God
   Become saved, sin no more:
   Become saved, sin no more,
   Become saved, sin no more;
   Until all saved church HIS God
   Become saved, sin no more.

4. Always since through faith I saw blood
   YOUR flowing wounds give,
   Saving[4] love has been my theme,[5]
   And shall continue until I die:
   And shall continue until I die,
   And shall continue until I die;
   Saving love has been my theme,
   And shall continue until I die.

Words, William Cowper, c. 1771.

---

[1] Make the sign for "water flow" or "river," if you don't know the sign for "fountain."

Strike the heart area twice with the right "G" hand, palm facing left and slightly downward. Make sign for "awful" in place of "guilty," if you prefer.
Use "God's Son" or just "Son" instead of "Lamb," if you wish.
Make the sign for "save" with both "R" hands when using "redeeming."
Make the sign for "quotation mark."

Beneath the Cross of Jesus   51

Under cross HIS Jesus I gladly[1] will take my stand,
Black shape of strong rock Inside tired land;
Home inside dry land, Rest on way,
From burning of noon heat And burden of day.

On cross HIS Jesus My eye at times can see
That dying shape HIS One[2] Who suffered there for me;
And from my guilty[3] heart with tears Two wonders[4] I confess,
Wonders HIS glorious[5] love And my not worthiness.[6]

I accept, O Cross, your black shape For my living place;
I ask no other sunshine than Sunshine HIS face;
Satisfied let world go away, Know no gain or loss,
My sinful self my only shame, My glory all cross.

Words, Elizabeth C. Clephane, 1872.

You may sign "willingly" in place of "gladly."
You may sign "Jesus" instead of "One."
Strike the heart area twice with the right "G" hand, palm facing left and slightly downward.
Make the sign for "wonderful."
Make the sign for "glory."
Make the sign for "worth" or "worthy."

1. When I study that wonderful cross,
   Where Jesus King from glory died,
   My richest earning seems as nothing,
   And I feel ashamed about my pride.

2. Lord, don't let me boast,
   Except about death Jesus my God;
   All worldly things that thrill me most,
   I sacrifice[1] to HIS blood.

3. See from Jesus' head, hands, feet,
   Sorrow and love flow;
   ? never before same love and sorrow join,
   Or thorns make truly beautiful crown?

4. ? all nature[2] became mine,
   That gift still very small;
   Love truly wonderful, truly divine,[3]
   Requires my soul, my life, my all. Amen.

Words, Isaac Watts, 1707.

[1] Make the sign for "offer," beginning with both hands in "S" position and ending with them the opening position.
[2] Make the sign for "world." If you like, you may make a sign for "world" with both "N" hands.
[3] Make the sign for "holy" with the right "D" hand.

Jesus Christ is[1] risen today, Alleluia![2]
Our victory holy day, Alleluia!
Who died once, on cross, Alleluia!
Suffer save[3] our souls. Alleluia!

Song with praise then let us sing, Alleluia!
To Christ, our heavenly King, Alleluia!
Who through[4] cross and grave, Alleluia!
Sinners redeem and save. Alleluia!

But pain HE suffered, Alleluia!
Our salvation have[5] received; Alleluia!
Now above sky HE is King, Alleluia!
Where angels always sing: Alleluia!

Sing we to our God above, Alleluia!
Praise forever HIS love; Alleluia!
Praise HIM, all you heavenly host,[6] Alleluia!
Father, Son, and Holy Spirit. Alleluia!

ords, st. 1, 14th Century Latin Hymn; translated in *Lyra Davidica*, 1708; st. 2, 3, Arnold's
mpleat Psalmodist, 1749; st. 4, Charles Wesley, 1740.

Make the sign for "truly."
Place both "A" hands in front of self and move them around twice, the right hand in the clockwise
direction and the left hand in the counter-clockwise motion. Then make the sign for "praise"
wice. The entire length of sign should coincide with the rhythm of "Alleluia."
Make the sign for "save" with both "R" hands when using "redeem."
Make the sign for "suffer" in place of "through," if you prefer.
Make the sign for "finish."
Make the sign for "class" at the eye or forehead level.

54   Low in the Grave He Lay

1. Low in grave HE lay, Jesus my Savior!
   Waiting coming day, Jesus my Lord!

2. For nothing soldiers watched HIS grave, Jesus my Savior!
   For nothing soldiers guarded dead, Jesus my Lord!

3. Death can't keep his prisoner, Jesus my Lord!
   HE broke jail,[1] Jesus my Lord!

REFRAIN:

   Up from grave HE arose,
   With powerful victory over HIS enemy;
   HE arose victor[2] from dark prison,
   And HE lives forever with HIS people control.
   HE arose! HE arose!
   Hallelujah![3] Christ arose!

Words, Robert Lowry, 1874.

[1] Death is like a jail. Christ won over death. Sign "HE destroyed death, Jesus my Lord!" instead of "He broke jail, Jesus my Lord!" if you prefer. Sign "He arose victor from death" instead of "He arose victor from dark jail," if you wish.
[2] Make the sign for "victory" ending with the sign for "er" as in "teacher." Make the sign for "winner."
[3] Make the sign for "praise" + "victory." Make the sign for "H" with both hands to be followed by the sign for "praise" + "victory," if you want.

Angels rolled stone from door,
As in grave HE lay;
God raised HIM, our living Lord,
And made first Lord's Day.

Birds that sang, flowers that bloomed,
Both brought no joy[1] that spring,
Until Christ was[2] raised from death become
Our living Lord and King.

All earth is full with green today,
Welcome our risen Lord;
We praise, because HE lives again,
HE keeps HIS promised word.

REFRAIN:

We sing for joy, we sing for joy,
With loving thanks we say:
"God raised HIM, our living Lord,
And made first Lord's Day."

Words, William N. McElrath, 1964. © Copyright 1964 Broadman Press. All rights reserved.

Make the sign for "happy" with one or both hands.
Make the sign for "true" or "truly."

1. My faith has found resting place,
   Not in invention or religious saying;
   I trust Everlasting[1] One,
   HIS wounds for me shall beg.

2. Enough for me that Jesus saves,
   This melts[2] my fear and doubt;
   Sinful soul I come to HIM,
   HE will never throw me out.

3. My heart is depending on Word,
   Written Word HIS God,
   Salvation through my Savior's name,
   Salvation through HIS blood.

4. My wonderful Doctor heals sick,
   Lost HE came save;
   For me HIS sweet, important blood HE gave,
   For me HIS life HE gave.

REFRAIN:

   I need no other argument,[3]
   I need no other beg,
   This is enough that Jesus died,
   And that HE died for me.

Words, Lidie H. Edmunds, 19th Century.

---

[1] Make the sign for "forever."
[2] Make the sign for "stop" or "end" if you wish.
[3] Make the sign for "argue."

Baptist, 1975—380

Rejoice,[1] Lord is King:
Your Lord and King love-worship!
Rejoice, give thanks and sing,
And victory forever:
Lift your heart, lift your voice![2]
Rejoice, again I say, rejoice!

Jesus, Savior, controls,
God HIS truth and love;
When HE had cleaned our sins,
HE took HIS seat above:
Lift your heart, lift your voice!
Rejoice, again I say, rejoice!

HIS kingdom cannot fail,
HE controls over earth and heaven;
Keys of death and hell
Are to our Jesus given:
Lift your heart, lift your voice!
Rejoice, again I say, rejoice!

Rejoice in glorious[3] hope!
Our Lord and judge shall come
And take HIS people[4]
To their forever home:
Lift your heart, lift your voice!
Rejoice, again I say, rejoice! Amen.

ords, Charles Wesley, 1744.

Make the sign for "happy" with one or both hands. The use of both hands looks better.
Make the sign for "hands" instead of "voice" if you wish.
Make the sign for "glory."
Make the sign for "servants" if you prefer.

1. I know my Redeemer[1] lives,
   And on earth again will stand;
   I know eternal[2] life HE gives,
   Grace and power are in HIS hand.

2. I know HIS promise never fails,
   Word HE speaks cannot die;
   No matter awful death my body destroys,
   Still I shall see HIM future.[3]

3. I know my beautiful home HE prepares,
   Then where HE lives there I will live;
   O wonderful thought, HE loves me,
   And finally HE will come take me.

REFRAIN:

   I know, I know Jesus lives,
   And on earth again will stand;
   I know, I know life HE gives,
   Grace and power are in HIS hand.

Words, Jessie Brown Pounds, 1893.

---

[1] Make the sign for "Savior." If you wish, you can make the sign for "Savior" with both "R" hand
[2] Make a sign for "forever." If you like, you may make a sign for "forever" with the right "
hand.
[3] Sign "future" very slowly to keep in rhythm with the music.

Holy Spirit, breathe on me,
Until my heart becomes clean;
Let sunshine fill all my heart,
Without one black cloud bothering.

Holy Spirit, breathe on me,
My stubborn wants overcome;
Teach me with words as living fire
What Jesus wants me do.

Holy Spirit, breathe on me,
Fill me with power divine;[1]
Begin fire love and eagerness[2]
In this heart mine.

Holy Spirit, breathe on me,
Until I become fully YOURS,
Until my wants become same[3] YOURS,
Living for YOU alone.

REFRAIN:

Breathe on me, breathe on me,
Holy Spirit, breathe on me;
YOU take my heart,
Cleanse[4] every part,
Holy Spirit, breathe on me.

Words, Edwin Hatch, 1878; adapted, B. B. McKinney, 1937. Copyright 1937; Renewal 1965 Broadman Press. All rights reserved.

Make the sign for "holy" with the right "D" hand.
Make the sign for "eager," "willing," or "enthusiasm."
Make the sign for "as," "also," or "too."
Make the sign for "wash clean" or "clean."

60   Come, Holy Spirit, Heavenly Dove

1. Come, Holy Spirit, Heavenly Bird,
   With all YOUR life-giving powers,
   Begin burning fire of holy love
   In cold hearts of ours.

2. Without success we start our cold songs;
   Without success we try stand;
   Hosannas[1] weak on our tongues,
   And our worship dies.

3. Come, Holy Spirit, Heavenly Bird,
   With all YOUR life-giving powers,
   Come, spread[2] Savior's love,
   And that shall start burning ours.[3]

Words, Isaac Watts, 1707.

---

[1] Make the sign for "H" with both hands; then, the sign for "praise."
[2] Make the signs for "give us" instead of "spread," if you want.
[3] Make the sign for "our love" in place of just "ours," if you wish.

Baptist, 1975—134   Baptist, 1956—169   Broadman—26

61   Spirit of the Living God

Spirit from living God, come new on me;[1]
Spirit from living God, come new on me.
Change me, humble me, make me, fill me.
Spirit from living God, come new on me.

Words, Daniel Iverson, 1926.

---

[1] Sign "come to me," if you wish.

Baptist, 1975—136   Baptist, 1956—523   Broadman—32

Holy Spirit, Light divine,[1]
Shine on this heart mine;
Take black shape from night away,[2]
Change my darkness to day.

Holy Spirit, Power divine,
Clean this guilty[3] heart mine;
Long has sin, without control,
Had[4] power over my soul.

Holy Spirit, Joy divine,
Cheer this sad heart mine;
Make my many troubles melt,[5]
Heal my sore, bleeding[6] heart.

Holy Spirit, all divine,
Live within[7] this heart mine;
Break[8] every sinful throne;
Control highest and control alone. Amen.

Words, Andrew Reed, 1817, alt.

Make sign for "holy" with the right "D" hand, palm facing down. Make sign for "holy" instead of "divine," if you want.
This line shows that each person's life is dark with sin; but when he lets the Holy Spirit live in his heart, a person walks in God's light.
Strike heart area with right "G" hand, palm facing left. If you don't know how to sign "guilty," make sign for "wrong."
Make sign for "hold," if you want.
Sign "Tell my many troubles leave," if you like.
Make sign for "blood."
Make sign for "inside" near heart area.
Make the sign for "throw down" or "destroy," if you want.

1. Holy Bible, Book divine,[1]
   Sweet, important Book, truly mine:
   Mine for telling me from where I come;
   Mine for teaching me what I am.[2]

2. My Book for scolding me when I stray,
   Mine for showing Savior's love;
   Mine truly for leading and protecting;
   Mine for punishing and rewarding.[3]

3. My Book for comforting during trouble,
   Suffering in this world full sin;
   Mine for showing through living faith,
   People can win overcoming death.

4. My Book for telling me about happy future,
   And disobedient[4] sinner's future punishment;[5]
   O that Holy Book divine,
   Sweet, important Book, truly mine.

Words, John Burton, Sr., 1803.

---

[1] Make the sign for "holy" with the right "D" hand.
[2] Make the sign for "truly."
[3] Make the sign for "gift."
[4] Make the sign for "disobey" or "not obey."
[5] Make the sign for "punish."

Break YOU bread of [1] life, Loving Lord, to me,
Same you before[2] broke leaf Near sea;
Through holy Word[3] I seek YOU, Lord;
My spirit breathes[4] for YOU, O living Word.

Bless YOU truth, loving Lord, To me, to me,
Same YOU before bless bread Near Galilee;[5]
Then shall all slavery[6] stop, All chains fall,[7]
And I shall find my peace, My all in all.

YOU are[8] bread of life, O Lord, to me,
YOUR holy Word truth That saves me;
Give me eat and live With YOU above;
Teach me love YOUR truth, Because YOU are love.

O send YOUR Spirit, Lord, Now to me,
That HE can touch my eyes, And make me see:
Show me truth hidden[9] Inside YOUR Word,
And in YOUR Book shown I see Lord. Amen.

Words, st. 1, 2, Mary A. Lathbury, 1877; st. 3, 4, Alexander Groves, 1913.

You may sign "giving" in place of "of" if you feel this will help convey a meaning.
Make the sign for "past" or "long ago."
You may make the sign for "Bible," if you wish.
You may sign either "thirst" or "hunger" if you feel this is clearer.
You may either spell the word "Galilee" or make a sign for "sea."
Make the sign for "slave."
Instead of making the sign for "join," do the opposite with this sign to show the "breaking of chains."
Make the sign for "truly."
Make the sign for "hide."

1. Sing again and again to me,
   Wonderful words about life;
   Let me more about their beauty see,
   Wonderful words about life;
   Words about life and beauty,
   Teach me faith and duty:

2. Jesus, that wonderful One, gives to all people
   Wonderful words about life;
   Sinner, hear HIS loving call,
   Wonderful words about life;
   All truly freely given,
   Leading us to heaven:

3. Sweetly listen[1] that gospel[2] call,
   Wonderful words about life;
   Offer pardon[3] and peace to all,
   Wonderful words about life;
   Jesus, only Savior,
   Make clean forever.

REFRAIN:

   Beautiful words, wonderful words,
   Wonderful words about life;
   Beautiful words, wonderful words,
   Wonderful words about life.

Words, Philip P. Bliss, 1874.

---

[1] If you like, you may sign "tell again" instead of "listen."
[2] Make the sign for "new" with the right "G" hand, the palm facing left.
[3] Make the sign for "forgive."

1. Faith from our fathers! living still
   No matter jail, fire, and sword,
   O truly our hearts beat[1] with joy[2]
   When we hear that glorious[3] word!
   Faith from our fathers, holy faith!
   We will continue true to faith[4] until death.

2. Faith from our fathers! we will try
   Win all nations to faith,
   And through truth that comes from God
   People shall then become truly free:
   Faith from our fathers, holy faith!
   We will continue true to faith until death.

3. Faith from our fathers! we will love
   Both friend and enemy in all our fighting,
   And preach faith, too, as love knows how
   Through kind words and clean life:
   Faith from our fathers, holy faith!
   We will continue true to faith until death.

Words, Frederick W. Faber, 1849.

Touch the heart area with the right "A" hand, palm facing self, about two times, with the left
and covering the right hand. Make the sign for "felt" instead of "beat," if you prefer.
Make the sign for "happy" with one or both hands.
Make the sign for "glory."
Make the sign for "that faith" in place of "faith," if you like.

1. God of our fathers, whose powerful hand
   Leads forward in beauty all starry group[1]
   Of shining worlds in beauty through sky,
   Our thankful songs before YOUR throne offer.

2. YOUR love divine has led us in past,[2]
   In this free land through YOU our life is given;
   Continue YOU our ruler,[3] protector,[4] leader, and helper,
   YOUR Word our law, YOUR paths our chosen way.

3. From war dangers, from awful sickness,[5]
   Continue YOUR strong arms our always sure defense;
   YOUR true religion[6] in our hearts grow,
   YOUR plenty goodness[7] feed us in peace.

4. Strengthen[8] YOUR people on their working way,
   Lead us from night to never ending[9] day;
   Fill all our lives with love and grace divine,
   And glory, honor, and praise be always YOURS. Amen.

Words, Daniel C. Roberts, 1876.

---

[1] Make the sign for "class" at the eye or forehead level.
[2] Make the sign for "past" or "long ago."
[3] Make the sign for "control," ending with the sign for "er" as in "teacher."
[4] Make the sign for "protect," ending with the sign for "er."
[5] Make the sign for "sick."
[6] Touch the heart area with fingertips of right "R" hand, palm facing self; then, move right "R" hand forward, fingertips pointing slightly forward.
[7] Make the sign for "good."
[8] Make the sign for "strength" or "strong." Sign "make strong" or "give strength to" instead of "strengthen," if you wish.
[9] Make sign for "forever," if you like.

Baptist, 1975—149   **Baptist, 1956—54**   **Broadman—22**

. This is my Father's world,
And to my listening ears,
All nature[1] sings, And around me sings
Music[2] of earth.
This is my Father's world,
I comfort myself with thinking
About rocks and trees, about sky and sea;
HIS hands wonderfully made.

. This is my Father's world,
Birds their songs offer;
Morning light, flower white
Announce their Maker's praise.
This is my Father's world.
HE shines in all that is beautiful;
Through windy green-growing I hear HIM walk,
HE speaks to me everywhere.

. This is my Father's world,
O let me never forget
That no matter wrong seems often strong,
God is Ruler still,
This is my Father's world,
War is not finished;
Jesus who died shall be satisfied,
And earth and heaven become one.

Words, Maltbie D. Babcock, 1901.

---

[1] Make the sign for "world." If you wish, you may make the sign for "world" with both "N" hands.
[2] Make the sign for "song."

1. I hear Savior say,
   "Your strength really small,
   Child weak, look up and pray,
   Find in ME your all in all.

2. Lord, now really I find
   YOUR power, and YOURS alone,
   Can change sinner's life
   And melt heart full hard.

3. For nothing good have I
   YOUR grace demand;[1]
   I will make my life clean
   Through blood from Jesus on cross.

4. And when before[2] throne,
   I stand in HIM free,
   "Jesus died my soul save,"
   My lips shall say again and again.

REFRAIN:

   Jesus paid it all,
   All to HIM I owe;
   Sin left red spot,[3]
   He washed that white as snow.

Words, Elvina M. Hall, 1865.

---

[1] Make the sign for "require" or "earn."
[2] Make the sign for "presence."
[3] Make the sign for "splash" by beginning with the right "O" hand and then spreading it again
the left open hand so as to "splash" it.

1. ? sad, true my Savior bleed[1]
And true my Lord died?
? Jesus give HIS holy life
For sinner as me?

2. ? true for sins I have[2] done
Jesus suffered on cross?
True wonderful mercy, grace no limit,
And love above my understanding!

3. True right for sun in darkness[3] hide,
And close heaven's glory in.
When Jesus powerful[4] Maker died,
For people's sin.

4. But my grief can't cancel[5]
Love debt I owe;
Now, Lord, I give myself to YOU,
Truly all I can do.

REFRAIN:

At cross, at cross there I first understood,
And burden from my heart disappears,[5]
True there through faith I received understanding
And now I am[6] happy all day.

Words, Isaac Watts, 1707; Refrain, Ralph E. Hudson, 1885.

Make the sign for "blood."
Make the sign for "finish."
Make the sign for "dark."
Make the sign for "power."
Make the sign for "melt."
Make the sign for "truly."

71   Nothing but the Blood

1. ? what can wash clean my sin
   Nothing except[1] blood from Jesus;
   ? what can make me clean again
   Nothing except blood from Jesus.

2. For my pardon[2] this I see,
   Nothing except blood from Jesus;
   For my cleansing, this my prayer,
   Nothing except blood from Jesus.

3. Nothing can for sin atone,[3]
   Nothing except blood from Jesus;
   Nothing good I have done,
   Nothing except blood from Jesus.

4. This is all my hope and peace,
   Nothing except blood from Jesus;
   This is all my righteousness,[4]
   Nothing except blood from Jesus.

REFRAIN:

Oh! sweet, important is blood
That makes me white as snow;
No other help I know,
Nothing except blood from Jesus.

Words, Robert Lowry, 1876.

---

[1] You may use the sign for "but" if you like it better.
[2] Make a sign for "forgive."
[3] Make a sign for "exchange" or "pay."
[4] You may make a sign for "doing right" if you feel that these words are clearer.

Will you be

1. Want[1] you free from burden full sin?
   There is[2] power in blood, power in blood;
   Want you over evil victory win?
   There is wonderful power in blood.

2. Want you free from your hunger and pride?
   There is power in blood, power in blood;
   Come for cleaning to mountain-cross' blood;
   There is wonderful power in blood.

3. Want you become white, much whiter than snow?
   There is power in blood, power in blood;
   Sins are washed in life-giving blood;
   There is wonderful power in blood.

4. Want you really work for Jesus your King?
   There is power in blood, power in blood;
   Want you live every day HIS praises sing?
   · There is wonderful power in blood.

REFRAIN:

There is power, power, Wonderful working power
In blood HIS Jesus;
There is power, power, Wonderful working power
In sweet, important blood HIS Jesus.

Words, Lewis E. Jones, 1899.

Make the sign for "Would" or "Will you be," if you prefer.
Make the sign for "truly."

1. I have[1] found a friend who is[2] all to me,
   HIS love is always true;
   I love tell how Jesus lifted me,
   And what HIS grace can do for you.

2. Jesus saves me from each sin and danger,
   Protects my soul each day;
   I depend fully on HIS strong arms;
   I know HE leads me all my way.

3. When weak and without help and alone,
   With love HE said to me,
   Come to ME and I will lead you home,
   For living with ME eternally.[3]

REFRAIN:

   Saved through HIS power divine,[4]
   Saved to new life highest!
   Life now is sweet and my happiness is full,
   Because I am saved, saved, saved.

Words, Jack P. Scholfield, 1911.

[1] Make the sign for "finish."
[2] Make the sign for "truly."
[3] Make the sign for "forever." You can make the sign for "forever" with the right "E" hand.
[4] Make the sign for "holy" with the "D" hand.

1. I must go home through way of cross,
   There is[1] no other way except[2] this;
   I shall never get see gate bright,
   If way of cross I miss.

2. I must go in blood-sprinkled way,
   Way[3] that Savior walked,
   If I anytime reach heaven wonderfully,[4]
   Where soul is at home with God.

3. Then I say good-bye to way of world,
   Walk in way never more;
   Because my Lord says "Come," and I seek my home,
   Where HE waits at open door.

REFRAIN:

   Way of cross leads home,
   Way of cross leads home;
   Truly sweet know as I onward go,
   Way of cross leads home.

Words, Jessie B. Pounds, 1906.

[1] Make the sign for "truly."
[2] Make the sign for "but," if you prefer.
[3] You may make the sign for "way" with both "P" hands when using "path."
[4] Make the sign for "wonderful."

1. Rock forever, open for me,
   Let me hide myself in YOU;
   Let water and blood,
   From YOUR wounded[1] side flowed,
   Become for sin twice cure,[2]
   Save from anger[3] and made me pure.

2. Not work from my hands
   Can satisfy law's demands;[4]
   Can my zeal[5] no rest know,
   Can my tears forever flow,[6]
   All for sin cannot forgive;
   YOU must save, and YOU alone.

3. While I have this last breath,
   When my eyes shall close in death,
   When I reach heaven,
   And see YOU on YOUR throne,
   Rock forever, open for me,
   Let me hide myself in YOU. Amen.

Words, Augustus M. Toplady, 1775, 1776.

---

[1] Make the sign for "sore" or "wound."
[2] Make the sign for "heal" or "well."
[3] Make the sign for "angry" or "mad."
[4] Make the sign for "require."
[5] Make the sign for "willing" or "enthusiasm." Rub both open, flat hands, palms facing each other, forward and backward two or three times.
[6] Make the sign for "weep" by touching both eyes with tips of both index fingers, both hands being open and palms facing self, and moving both hands downward while wiggling the fingers.

. Have[1] you been[2] to Jesus for cleaning power?
Are you washed in blood HIS Jesus?[3]
Are you fully trusting in HIS grace right now?
Are you washed in blood HIS Jesus?

2. Are you walking daily near Savior's side?
Are you washed in blood HIS Jesus?
Really you rest each minute in Jesus?
Are you washed in blood HIS Jesus?

3. When Jesus comes, will your robes be white?
Are you washed in blood HIS Jesus?
Will your soul be ready for heaven bright,
And be washed in blood HIS Jesus?

4. Put away[4] lives[5] that are dirty with sin,
And be washed in blood HIS Jesus;
There is blood flowing for soul not clean,
O be washed in blood HIS Jesus.

REFRAIN:

Are you washed in blood,
In soul-cleaning blood HIS Jesus?
Are your lives clean? Are your lives white as snow?
Are you washed in blood HIS Jesus?

Words, Elisha A. Hoffman, 1878.

Make the sign for "finish."
Make the sign for "true" or "truly."
Make the sign for "Lamb," if you wish.
Make the sign for "put down" instead of "put away," if you wish.
Make the sign for "souls" if you feel that word is clear. Or, make the sign for "clothes" if the
deaf understand the abstract idea. See the first line of stanza 3 and change "robes" for "lives"
or "souls," if you want. If so, use "clean" instead of "white" when using "lives."

77   Amazing Grace! How Sweet the Sound

1. Wonderful grace! truly sweet that word,
   That saved sinner as me!
   I before[1] was[2] lost, but now I am found,
   Was blind, but now I can see.

2. Truly grace taught my heart fear,
   And grace my fears removed;[3]
   Truly sweet, important that grace becomes
   That hour I first believed.

3. Through many dangers, hard work, and temptations,
   I have[4] come;
   Truly grace has brought me safe to now,
   And grace will lead me home.

4. Lord has promised good to me,
   HIS word my hope protects;
   HE will my protection[5] and part become
   As long as life continues.

5. When we have lived in heaven ten thousand years,
   Bright shining as sun,
   We still have more days for singing God's praise
   Than when we first began. Amen.

Words, st. 1-4, John Newton, 1779; st. 5, Anonymous.

---

[1] Make the sign for "past."
[2] These lines show that we were lost in sin as sheep were lost from the pasture, Jesus the good Shepherd found us, the lost "sheep." We were blind in sin, but now we know or understand God's truth.
[3] Make the sign for "take away" or "take out."
[4] Make the sign for "finish."
[5] Make the sign for "protect."

1. Many years I lived foolish and proud,
   Interested not my Lord was crucified,
   Knowing not for me Jesus died
   On mountain-cross.

2. Through God's Word about my sin I learned;
   Then I feared because HIS law I had broken,
   Until my guilty[1] soul begging looked
   To mountain-cross.

3. Now I have given Jesus everything,
   Now I gladly accept HIM as my King,
   Now my happy soul can only sing
   About mountain-cross.

4. Oh, wonderful love that made salvation plan!
   Oh, wonderful grace that offered salvation to people!
   Oh, wonderful salvation God truly gave
   At mountain-cross.

REFRAIN:

   Mercy there was much, and grace was free;
   Forgiveness[2] there was given to me;
   There my guilty soul found salvation,
   At mountain-cross.

Words, William R. Newell, 1895.

---

[1] Strike at least twice the heart area with the right "G" hand, palm facing slightly left and downward.
You may make the sign for "sinful," instead.
[2] Make the sign for "forgive" or "pardon."

1. Sinners Jesus will accept:
   Spread this word about grace to all
   Who heavenly pathway[1] leave,
   All who wait, all who sin.[2]

2. Come, and HE will give you peace:
   Trust HIM because HIS word is[3] clear;
   He will take awful sinner;
   Christ accepts sinful people.

3. Now my heart judges me not,
   Pure before[4] law I stand;
   HE who cleaned me from all sin,
   Satisfied law's last demand.[5]

4. Christ accepts sinful people,
   No matter me with all my sin;
   Cleaned from every sin and filth,[6]
   Heaven with HIM I enter.

REFRAIN:

   Sing story again and again;
   Christ accepts sinful people;
   Make story clear and true:
   Christ accepts sinful men.

Words, Erdmann Neumeister, 1718; translated, Emma F. Bevan, 1858.

---

[1] Make the sign for "way"; you can make the sign with both "P" hands.
[2] You may sign "fall in sin," if you wish.
[3] Make the sign for "truly."
[4] Make the sign for "presence."
[5] Make the sign for "require."
[6] Make the sign for "dirty."

1. To God give glory, wonderful things HE has[1] done;
   Truly loved HE world and gave us HIS Son,
   Jesus gave HIS life exchange for sin,
   And opened life-gate, then all HIS people can enter.

2. O perfect salvation,[2] bought with Jesus' blood,
   To every believer that promise from God;
   Worst sinner who truly believes,
   That minute from Jesus forgiveness[3] receives.

3. Wonderful things HE has taught us, wonderful things HE has done,
   And wonderful our joy[4] through Jesus God's Son;
   But purer, higher, more wonderful will become
   Our wonder, our victory, when Jesus we see.

REFRAIN:

   Praise Lord, praise Lord, Let people hear HIS voice!
   Praise Lord, praise Lord, Let people rejoice![4]
   O go to Father through Jesus HIS Son,
   And give God glory, wonderful things HE has done. Amen.

Words, Fanny J. Crosby, 1875.

Make the sign for "finish."
Make the sign for "salvation" with both "R" hands when using "redemption."
Make the sign for "forgive" or "pardon."
Make the sign for "happy," using both hands.

81   Lord, I'm Coming Home

1. I have wandered[1] far from God,
   Now I am going home;
   Paths[2] full sin long I have walked,
   Lord, I am going home.

2. I have wasted many sweet, important years,
   Now I am going home;
   I now repent with bitter tears,
   Lord, I am going home.

3. I am tired sinning and straying,
   Now I am going home;
   I will trust YOUR love, believe YOUR word,
   Lord, I am going home.

4. My soul is sick, my heart is sad,
   Now I am going home;
   My strength[3] made new, my hope made strong,[4]
   Lord, I am going home.

REFRAIN:

   Going home, going home,
   Never more wander;
   Open wide YOUR arm full love,
   Lord, I am going home.

Words, William J. Kirkpatrick, 1892.

---

[1] Make the sign for "stray."
[2] Make the sign for "way" with both "P" hands. You can sign "way," if you prefer.
[3] Make the sign for "strong."
[4] You may make the sign for "sure" or "true."

. I hear YOUR welcome voice
  That calls me, Lord, to YOU,
  For cleaning in YOUR sweet, important blood
  That flowed on mountain-cross.

. No matter weak and sinful,
  YOU really my strength make sure;
  YOU really my sinfulness[1] fully clean,
  Until sin none[2] all, and pure.

. Truly Jesus calls me on[3]
  To perfect faith and love,
  To perfect hope and peace and trust,
  For earth and heaven above.

. All welcome! forgiving blood!
  All welcome! saving[4] grace!
  All welcome! gift from Christ our Lord,
  Our strength and righteousness.[5]

REFRAIN:

  I am[6] coming, Lord!
  Coming now to YOU!
  Wash me, clean me in blood
  That flowed on mountain-cross!

Words, Lewis Hartsough, 1872.

Make the sign for "sin."
Make the sign for "perfect" instead of "sin none," if you want.
Make the sign for "forward" or "onward."
Make the sign for "saving" with both "'R'" hands when using "redeeming."
Make the sign for "right" by moving the right "R" hand, palm facing left, across the left, open hand, palm facing upward, in a forward motion. Make the sign for "right doing," if you want.
Make the sign for "true" or "truly."

1. Pass me not, O sweet Savior,
   Hear my humble shout;
   While on others YOU are[1] calling,
   Don't pass me away.

2. Let me at YOUR throne mercy
   Find sweet comfort;
   Kneeling there in deep sorrow,
   Help my not-belief.

3. Trusting only in YOUR goodness,[2]
   Will I see YOUR face;
   Heal my sore, broken spirit,
   Save me through YOUR grace.

4. YOU giver all my comfort,
   More than life to me,
   Whom have I on earth except[3] YOU?
   Whom in heaven except YOU?

REFRAIN:

   Savior, Savior,
   Hear my humble shout;
   While on others YOU are calling,
   Don't pass me away.

Words, Fanny J. Crosby, 1868.

---

[1] Make the sign for "truly."
[2] Make the sign for "good."
[3] Make the sign for "but" instead of "except," if you like.

. I have decided no longer wait,
Interested through world's pleasure;
Things that are higher, things that are good,
Things have attracted my eyes.

. I have decided go to Savior,
Leaving my sin and trouble;
HE is real one, HE is right one,
HE has words about life.

. I have decided follow Jesus,
Faithful and true each day;
Pay attention what HE says, do what HE wants,
HE is living way.

. I have decided enter kingdom,
Leaving paths of sin;
Friends may oppose me, enemies may bother me,
Still will I enter.

. I have decided, and who will go with me?
Come, friends, without waiting,
Taught through Bible, led through Spirit,
We will walk heavenly way.

REFRAIN:

I will hurry to Jesus,
Hurry truly glad and free,
Jesus, greatest, highest,
I will come to YOU.

Words, Palmer Hartsough, 1896.

1. Out from my slavery,[1] sorrow, and night,[2]
   Jesus, I come, Jesus, I come;
   Into YOUR freedom, gladness,[3] and light,
   Jesus, I come to YOU;
   Out from my sickness[4] into YOUR healing,
   Out from my poverty[5] and into YOUR wealth.[6]
   Out from my sin and into YOURSELF,
   Jesus, I come to YOU.

2. Out from my shameful failure[7] and loss,
   Jesus, I come, Jesus, I come;
   Into glorious[8] blessing through YOUR cross,
   Jesus, I come to YOU:
   Out from world's sorrows into YOUR comfort,
   Out from life's trouble into YOUR peace,
   Out from suffering to happy song,
   Jesus, I come to YOU.

3. Out from rebellious[9] and boastful pride,
   Jesus, I come, Jesus, I come;
   Into YOUR blessed want live-continue,
   Jesus, I come to YOU;
   Out from myself to live in YOUR love,
   Out from sadness[10] into joys above,
   Upward for always on wings like bird,
   Jesus, I come to YOU.

4. Out from fearful and awful thinking about death,
   Jesus, I come, Jesus, I come;
   Into joy and light for YOUR heavenly home,
   Jesus, I come to YOU;
   Out from dark sin that I can't explain,
   Into peace with YOUR protection,[11]
   Always YOUR glorious face look,[12]
   Jesus, I come to YOU.

Words, William T. Sleeper, *c.* 1887.

---

[1] Make the sign for "slave."
[2] Make the sign for "dark."

Make the sign for "happy" with one or both hands.
Make the sign for "sick" or "ill."
Make the sign for "poor."
Make the sign for "rich."
Make the sign for "fail."
Make the sign for "glory."
You may make the sign for "disobey," "not obey," or "restless."
Make the sign for "sad."
Make the sign for "protect" or "guard."
Make the sign for "see" or "watch."

Baptist, 1975—178   Baptist, 1956—233

"Whosoever Will"   86

"Who hears," shout, shout noise!
Spread happy story all world around;
Tell happy story where no matter man is[1] found,[2]
"Who want can come."

Who comes need not wait,[3]
Now door is open, enter while you can;
Jesus is real, only Living Way:
"Who want can come."

"Who want" promise is real;
"Who want," forever must continue;
"Who want," this life forever more:
"Who want can come."

REFRAIN:

"Who want can come. Who want, who want!"
Send announcement[4] over valley and hill;
This loving Father calls sinner home:
"Who want can come."

Words, Philip P. Bliss, 1869.

Make the sign for "truly."
Sign this line "Tell happy story where no matter we find man," if you prefer.
Make the sign for "put off," "delay," or "postpone," if you like this one better.
Make the sign for "story," if you wish.

Baptist, 1975—184   Baptist, 1956—238   Broadman—126

1. If you are[1] tired your heavy burden sin,
   Let Jesus come into your heart;
   If you want new life start,
   Let Jesus come into your heart.

2. If this for clean life now that you want,
   Let Jesus come into your heart;
   Jesus' blood for cleansing is given for you,
   Let Jesus come into your heart.

3. If there is trouble you can't solve,[2]
   Let Jesus come into your heart;
   If truly emptiness[3] this world never can fill,
   Let Jesus come into your heart.

4. If you will join glad songs for happy Christians,
   Let Jesus come into your heart;
   If you want enter heaven for rest,
   Let Jesus come into your heart.

REFRAIN:

   Exact now, your doubts surrender;[4]
   Exact now, refuse HIM no more;
   Exact now, open wide door;
   Let Jesus come into your heart.

Words, Leila N. Morris, 1898.

---

[1] Make the sign for "truly."
[2] Make the sign for "melt" or "disappear."
[3] Make the sign for "empty."
[4] Make the sign for "give up."

. Ruler[1] once came to Jesus through night
Ask HIM way showing salvation and light;
Master made answer in words true and clear,
"You must be born again."

. You children from people, listen to word
Truly important said Jesus Lord;
And let not this message[2] to you become nothing,
"You must be born again."

. O you who want enter that glorious[3] rest,
And sing with saved people song of Christians,[4]
Life forever if you want get,
"You must be born again."

. Loving one in heaven your heart wants see,
At beautiful door may be watching for you,
Then listen to song of these important words,[5]
"You must be born again."

REFRAIN:

"You must be born again,
You must be born again.
I truly, truly say to you,
You must be born again."

Words, William T. Sleeper, 1877.

Make the sign for "control" ending with the sign for "er" as in "teacher."
Make the sign for "story" in place of "message," if you prefer.
Make the sign for "glory."
Make the sign for "blessed," if you prefer.
Make the sign for "story" instead of "words," if you like.

Only Trust Him

1. Come, every soul no matter sin burdened,
   There is mercy from Lord.
   And HE will surely give you rest
   Through trusting in HIS word.

2. For Jesus gave HIS sweet, important blood
   Wonderful blessings give;
   Enter now that red blood
   That washes white as snow.

3. Yes, Jesus is truth, way,
   That leads you into rest;
   Believe in HIM without postponing,[1]
   And you are fully happy.

4. Come, then, and join this holy people,[2]
   And on[3] to glory go,
   Live in that heavenly land,
   Where joys[4] forever continue.

REFRAIN:

   Only trust Him, only trust Him,
   Only trust HIM now;
   HE will save you, HE will save you,
   HE will save you now.

Words, John H. Stockton, *c.* 1873.

---

[1] Make the sign for "put off" or "delay."
[2] You may make the sign for "group."
[3] Make the sign for "forward" or "onward."
[4] Make the sign for "happy" with one or both hands.

Exact as I am without one excuse,
But YOUR blood was given for me,
And because YOU invite me go to YOU,
O Lamb from God, I come! I come!

Exact as I am, and waiting not
For removing[1] from my soul one black sin,
To YOU whose blood can wash each sin,
O Lamb from God, I come! I come!

Exact as I am, no matter bothered
With many troubles, many doubt,
Fighting within[2] and fears without,[3]
O Lamb from God, I come! I come!

Exact as I am, poor, sad, blind;
Sight, riches, good mind,
Yes, all I need in YOU find,
O Lamb from God, I come! I come!

Exact as I am, YOU will receive,
Will welcome, forgive, make clean and free,
Because YOUR promise I believe,
O Lamb from God, I come! I come!

Exact as I am, YOUR love not known
Has destroyed every sin,
Now become YOURS, yes, YOURS alone,
O Lamb from God, I come! I come!

ords, Charlotte Elliott, 1834.

Make the sign for "take away" or "remove."
Make the sign for "inside," with the left fingers and thumb touching the heart or chest area.
Make the sign for "outside," with the left fingers and thumb touching the heart or chest area.
This is the opposite of "within."

1. Lord Jesus, I want become perfectly clean;
   I want YOU forever save my soul;
   Destroy every sin, throw out[1] every enemy;
   Now wash me, and I shall become whiter than snow.

2. Lord Jesus, for this I truly humbly beg;
   I wait, wonderful Lord, at your crucified[2] feet;
   Through faith for my cleaning I see YOUR blood flow:
   Now wash me, and I shall become whiter than snow.

3. Lord Jesus, YOU know I patiently wait;
   Come now, and inside me new heart make;
   To all who seek YOU, YOU never say No:
   Now wash me, and I shall become whiter than snow.

REFRAIN:

Whiter than snow, yes, whiter than snow;
Now wash me, and I shall become whiter than snow.

Words, James Nicholson, 1872.

[1] You may make the sign for "take away" or "remove" in place of "throw out."
[2] Hit the left open palm with the closed right hand, palm facing the left shoulder; then, the rig
open hand with the left closed hand, palm facing the right shoulder. Then, spread out both arm
both palms facing forward, as if hung on a cross.

Jesus is[1] softly calling you home,
Calling today, calling today;
Why from sunshine full love will you stray
Far and far away?

Jesus is calling sin-tired (people) rest,
Calling today, calling today;
Bring HIM your burden and you will become happy;
HE will not push you away.

Jesus is waiting; O come to HIM now,
Waiting today, waiting today;
Come with your sins; at HIS feet humbly kneel;
Come and no more postpone.[2]

Jesus is begging; O listen to HIS voice,
Hear HIM today, hear HIM today;
People who believe on HIS name shall become happy;
Hurriedly[3] get up and go (to Jesus).

REFRAIN:

Calling today, Calling today,
Jesus is calling, Is softly calling today.

Words, Fanny J. Crosby, 1883.

Make the sign for "truly."
Make the sign for "put off" or "delay."
Make the sign for "hurry" or "quick."

1. My life, my love I give to YOU,
   YOU Lamb[1] from God who died for me;
   O let me always faithful[2] continue,
   My Savior and my God!

2. I now believe YOU truly accept me,
   Because YOU have[3] died that I can live;
   And from now on I will trust in YOU,
   My Savior and my God!

3. O YOU who died on mountain-cross,
   Save my soul and make me free,
   I will consecrate[4] my life to YOU,
   My Savior and my God!

REFRAIN:

I will live for HIM who died for me,
How happy then my life will become!
I will live for HIM who died for me,
My Savior and my God!

Words, Ralph E. Hudson, 1882.

---

[1] "Lamb" is one of many names for Jesus. Sign "Son" instead of "Lamb," if you prefer.
[2] Make the sign for "regular" with both "F" hands.
[3] Make the sign for "finish."
[4] Place in front of you both "C" hands, palms facing up. Then, move both hands upward whi
opening them into a sign for "offer."

Softly and sweetly Jesus is[1] calling,
Calling for you and for me;
See, in heaven HE is waiting and watching,
Watching for you and for me.

Why should we wait when Jesus is begging,
Begging for you and for me?
Why should we postpone[2] and not give attention to HIS mercies,
Mercies for you and for me?

Time is fast, minutes pass,
Pass from you and from me;
Darkness[3] more and more dark, death any time coming,
Coming for you and for me.

Oh! for that wonderful love HE has[4] promised,
Promised to you and to me;
No matter we have sinned, HE has mercy and forgiveness,
Forgiveness[5] for you and for me.

REFRAIN:

Come home, come home,
You who are tired come home;
Eagerly, sweetly, Jesus is calling,
Calling, sinner, come home.

Words, Will L. Thompson, 1880.

---

[1] Make the sign for "truly."
[2] Make the sign for "put off" or "delay."
[3] Make the sign for "dark."
[4] Make the sign for "finish."
[5] Make the sign for "forgive" or "pardon."

1. I will sing that wonderful story
   About Christ who died for me,
   How HE left HIS home in glory
   For that cross on mountain.

2. I was lost, but Jesus found me,
   Found me who strayed,
   Jesus put HIS arms around me,
   Led me again to HIS way.

3. I was sin-sick, but Jesus made me well;
   Spirit weak because many sins;
   Understanding nothing and fears control me;
   But HE freed me from all.

4. Days sad still come over me,
   Sorrow's way I often walk,
   But Savior still with me;
   With HIS hand HE safely led me.

5. Jesus will keep me until death's river
   Comes near me;
   Then HE will bring me safely to heaven,
   Where my loved people I will meet.

REFRAIN:

   Yes, I will sing wonderful story
   About Christ who died for me,
   Sing with saints in glory,
   Gathered near beautiful sea.

Words, Francis H. Rowley, 1886.

Come, you sinners, poor and needy,
Weak and wounded,[1] sick and sore;
Jesus ready stands save you,
Full with pity, love, and power.

Come, you thirsty, and welcome,
God's free gift glorify;[2]
True belief and true repentance,[3]
Every grace that brings you near.

Come, you tired, heavy burdened,
Lost and ruined through sin;
If you wait until you are better,
You will never come at all.

Let not conscience[4] make you wait,
Not about perfection[5] proudly dream;
All perfection HE requires
Is feel your need for HIM.

REFRAIN:

I will get up and go to Jesus,
HE will hug me in HIS arms;
In arms HIS my loving Savior,
O there are ten thousand pleasures.[6]

Words, Joseph Hart, 1759; Refrain, Anonymous.

Make the sign for "suffer" or "sore."
Make the sign for "glory."
Make the sign for "change" with both "R" hands near the heart area. If you cannot sign right, then make the sign for "confess."
Touch the heart area twice with the index finger of the right hand, palm facing left and slightly downward.
Make the sign for "perfect."
Make the sign for "enjoy" or "enjoyment" with both hands. Make the sign for "attract" or "interest," if you want.

1. Jesus waits welcome you,
   Will you come? Will you come?
   Arms HIS love outstretched[1] to you,
   Will you come? Will you come?

2. Jesus stands at mercy door,
   Will you come? Will you come?
   Pardon free Savior gives,
   Will you come? Will you come?

3. Peace and joy[2] you will have,
   Will you come? Will you come?
   Life forever[3] will be[4] yours,
   Will you come? Will you come?

4. Homes great[5] wait for you,
   Will you come? Will you come?
   Loving people you will meet again,
   Will you come? Will you come?

REFRAIN:

   Will you come? Will you come?
   O Savior invites you come;
   HE will welcome you with word full love,
   Will you come? Will you come?

Words, Isham E. Reynolds, *c.* 1920.

---

[1] Open wide your arms toward the person or group as if you want to receive them into your arm
[2] Make the sign for "happy" with one or both hands.
[3] Make the sign for "forever" with the right "E" hand when using "eternal."
[4] Make the sign for "true" or "truly."
[5] Make the sign for "wonderful," if you like this better than "great."

Baptist, 1975—199

Guide me, O YOU great God,
Travel through this dry land;
I am[1] weak, but YOU are strong,
Hold me with YOUR powerful hand;
Bread from heaven,
Feed me until I want no more;
Bread from heaven,
Feed me until I want no more.

Open now clear fountain[2]
Where healing waters flow;
Let fire and clouds
Lead me all my traveling through;
Strong Savior,
Be YOU continue my strength and protection;[3]
Strong Savior,
Be YOU continue my strength and protection.

When I walk near death,
Say that my worrying fear melt;
Carry me through time of death,
Bring me safe to heaven;
Songs of[4] praises
I will always give to YOU;
Songs of praises
I will always give to YOU.

Words, William Williams, 1745; translated, st. 1, Peter Williams, 1771; st. 2, 3, William Williams, 1772.

Make the sign for "truly."
Make the sign for "river" if you don't know the sign for "fountain."
Make the sign for "protect" or "defend."
Sign "with" instead of "of," if you prefer.

All the Way My Savior Leads Me

1. All way my Savior leads me;
   What need[1] I ask more?[2]
   Can I doubt HIS soft mercy,
   Who through life has been my guide?
   Heavenly peace, divine comfort,
   Here through faith in HIM live!
   Because I know what no matter happens to me,
   Jesus does all things good;
   Because I know what no matter happens to me,
   Jesus does all things good.

2. All way my Savior leads me,
   Cheers each straying path I walk,
   Gives me grace for every trouble,
   Feeds me with living word:
   No matter my tired feet may weaken,[3]
   And my soul thirsty may be,
   Overflowing[4] from Rock before me,
   Look! river of joy I see;
   Overflowing from Rock before me,
   Look! river of joy I see.

3. All way my Savior leads me,
   Oh, fullness[5] HIS love!
   Perfect rest to me is promised
   In my Father's house above:
   When my spirit, receiving life forever,
   Goes to heaven,
   This my song through never stopping years:[6]
   Jesus led me all way;
   This my song through never stopping years:
   Jesus led me all way.

Words, Fanny J. Crosby, 1875.

---

[1] Make the sign for "have," if you like that better.
[2] Use the sign for "other" in place of "more," if you wish.
[3] Make the sign for "weak."
[4] Make the sign for "pouring over" by moving the right hand up and over the semicupped le[...]
hand, both palms facing each other.
[5] Make the sign for "full."

Baptist, 1975—214   Baptist, 1956—268   Broadman—369

God Will Take Care of You   100

. Don't worry no matter what happens,
  God will watch over you;[1]
  Under HIS arms with love live-continue,
  God will watch over you.

. During days' work when your heart fails,
  God will watch over you;
  When trouble awful your way comes,[2]
  God will watch over you.

. No matter what your temptation,
  God will watch over you;
  Depend, you tired person, on HIM,
  God will watch over you.

REFRAIN:

God will watch over you,
Through every day, over all way;
HE will watch over you,
God will watch over you.

Words, Civilla D. Martin, 1905.

If you would rather use the words "Take care of," then you may sign "take keep" or just make
a sign for "keep" in a sweeping arc movement.
You may make the sign for "brother," if you like.

Baptist, 1975—219   Baptist, 1956—274

1. Savior, as shepherd lead us,
   Much we need YOUR loving care;
   In YOUR pretty green growing feed us,
   For our use YOUR home prepare;
   Blessed[1] Jesus, blessed Jesus,
   YOU have bought us, YOURS we are;
   Blessed Jesus, blessed Jesus,
   YOU have bought us, YOURS we are.

2. We are YOURS; truly YOU help us,
   Continue protector our way;
   Keep YOUR sheep from sin, protect us,
   Seek us when we go astray:[2]
   Blessed Jesus, blessed Jesus,
   Hear, O hear us when we pray;
   Blessed Jesus, blessed Jesus,
   Hear, O hear us when we pray.

3. YOU have promised receive us,
   Poor and sinful no matter we are;
   YOU have mercy for helping us,
   Grace for cleaning, and power for freeing:
   Blessed Jesus, blessed Jesus,
   Now let us turn to YOU;
   Blessed Jesus, blessed Jesus,
   Now let us turn to YOU.

4. Now let us seek YOUR favor;[3]
   Now let us do YOUR want;
   Blessed Lord and only Savior,
   With YOUR love our lives fill,
   Blessed Jesus, blessed Jesus,
   YOU have loved us, love us still;
   Blessed Jesus, blessed Jesus,
   YOU have loved us, love us still.

Words, Dorothy Thrupp's *Hymns for the Young,* 1836.

---

[1] Make the sign for "wonderful," if you wish.

Baptist, 1975—213   Baptist, 1956—344   Broadman—13

My Lord Is Near Me All the Time   102

In lightning bright across sky
HIS strong power I see,
And I know if HE can control on high,
HIS light can shine on me.

When thunder shakes powerful hills
And trembles[1] every tree,
Then I know God truly great and strong
Can surely protect[2] me.

When new rain cools earth
And sweep[3] across sea,
Then HIS rainbow shines within[4] my heart,
HIS nearness[5] comforts me.

REFRAIN:

I have seen that in lightning, heard that in thunder,
And felt that in rain;
My Lord is near me all time,
My Lord is near me all time.

Words, Barbara Fowler Gaultney, 1960. © Copyright 1960 Broadman Press. All rights reserved.

Place your arms in front of self, fingers spreading and tips pointing skyward. Move both hands rightward and leftward while shaking your body slightly as if showing the trees shaking or trembling during the storm.
Make the sign for "hide," if you want.
Make the sign for "blow" or "move," if you wish.
Make the sign for "inside" near the heart area.
Make the sign for "near."

Baptist, 1975—209

1. Live-continue[1] with me: fast comes evening;[2]
Evening becomes dark; Lord, with me live-continue:
When other helpers fail, and comforts leave,
Help for people without help, O live-continue with me!

2. Fast ends life's short day;
Earth's joy melts, earth's glory pass away;
Change and death in all around I see:
O YOU who change not, live-continue with me!

3. I need YOUR presence every passing hour;
What but[3] YOUR grace can break[4] tempter's[5] power?
Who as YOURSELF my leader and helper can become?
Through cloud[6] and sunshine, O live-continue with me!

4. Hold YOU YOUR cross before my closing eyes;
Shine through darkness, and show me to heaven:
Heaven's morning sunrise and earth's empty[7] darkness leave:
In life, in death, O Lord, live-continue with me! Amen.

Words, Henry F. Lyte, 1847.

---

[1] Make the sign for "stay" instead of "live-continue," if you prefer.
[2] This line is a picture of man's life. His life is compared (like) to a day. He is born like the mornin
that starts the day. He becomes a man at the top of his life like the noonday. Later, he become
an old man like the evening that is almost gone. When the night comes, everything stops.
is the same with a man when death comes to him. When he dies, he leaves his earthly life behin
He finds a new life in heaven. It is the same as a new morning or a new sunrise. Through h
life on earth, he finds that people often fail him. He turns to God for HIS help and presenc
(near him).
[3] Make the sign for "except," if you want.
[4] Make the sign for "destroy," if you wish.
[5] Make the sign for "tempt," ending with the sign for "er" as in "teacher." Make the sign fo
"devil" in place of "tempter," if you wish.
[6] Make the sign for "sorry" or "sad," if you want. If you use either one, be sure to use "happy
instead of "sunshine."
[7] Make the sign for "worthless" or "worth nothing," if you want.

. HE leads me! Truly wonderful thought!
Wonderful words with heavenly comfort given!
What no matter I do, where no matter I be,
Still this God HIS hand that leads me!

. Sometimes among places of deep darkness,[1]
Sometimes where beautiful places bloom,
Through waters still, over troubled sea,
Still this God HIS hand that leads me!

. Lord, I will hold YOUR hand in mine,
Not complain, not frown,[2]
Satisified, what no matter life I see,
Since this YOUR hand that leads me!

. And when my work on earth is finished,[3]
When, through YOUR grace, victory is won,
Even death's coming I will not escape,[4] *BE AFRaid*
Since God through death leads me!

REFRAIN:

HE leads me, HE leads me,
Through HIS own[5] hand HE leads me:
HIS faithful[6] follower I will become,
Because through HIS hand HE leads me.

Words, Joseph H. Gilmore, 1862.

Use "sad" in place of "dark," if you wish.
Make the sign for "angry" or "mad" by using your right hand in front of your face.
Make the sign for "done," if you like.
Make the sign for "fear," if you prefer.
Make the sign for "have" with both "O" hands, or omit it.
Make the sign for "regular" with both "F" hands.

1. O God, our help in years past,
   Our hope for years come,
   Our protection[1] from stormy[2] wind,
   And our forever[3] home!

2. Under black shape YOUR throne
   YOUR people have lived safely;
   Enough is YOUR arm alone,
   And our defense is sure.

3. Before hills in place stood,
   Or earth received round shape,[4]
   From forever[5] YOU are God,
   To never ending[6] years same.

4. One thousand years in YOUR eyes
   Are same evening gone;
   Short same watch[7] that ends night
   Before rising sun.

5. Time, same always rolling stream,
   Carries all its children away;
   Children fly, forgotten, as dream
   Dies at opening day.

6. O God, our help in years past,
   Our hope for years come,
   Continue YOU our guard while life shall continue,
   And our forever home. Amen.

Words, Isaac Watts, 1719.

---

[1] Make the sign for "protect."
[2] Make the sign for "awful," if you want.
[3] Make the sign for "forever" with the right "E" hand when using "eternal."
[4] Make the signs for "Or earth become ball," if you want.
[5] Make the sign for "forever" by moving the right "E" hand in a clockwise circle and moving the
   "Y" hand forward after it is changed from "E" to "Y" at the end of the circular motion.
[6] Make the signs for "never stopping," if you wish.

Make the sign for "watch" as a verb: "look," "see," "watch." Make the sign for "time" if you feel it is clearer than "watch."

Baptist, 1975—223   Baptist, 1956—286   Broadman—435

Follow On   106

1. There in valley with my Savior I will go,
   Where flowers are¹ blooming and sweet waters flow;
   Everywhere HE leads me I will follow, follow on,²
   Walking in HIS footsteps until crown be won.

2. There in valley with my Savior I will go,
   Where storms are blowing and dark waters flow;³
   With HIS hand lead me I will never, never fear,
   Danger can not fright⁴ me if my Lord is near.

3. There in valley or on mountain high,
   Near side my Savior will my soul always keep;
   HE will lead me safely in path⁵ HE has⁶ walked,
   Up to where others gather on hill HIS God.

REFRAIN:

   Follow! Follow! I will follow Jesus!
   Anywhere, everywhere, I will follow on!
   Follow! Follow! I will follow Jesus!
   Everywhere HE leads me, I will follow on!

Words, W. O. Cushing, 1880.

---

¹ Make the sign for "true" or "truly."
² Make the sign for "onward" or "forward."
³ This line is a picture of trouble and sorrow coming our way.
⁴ Make the sign for "scare," "frighten," or "afraid."
⁵ Make the sign for "way" with both "P" hands.
⁶ Make the sign for "finish."

Baptist, 1975—226   Broadman—118

Count Your Blessings

1. When through life's troubles you are much bothered,
   When you become discouraged,[1] thinking all is lost,
   Count your many blessings, name blessings one through one,
   And that will surprise you what Lord has done.

2. ? you always bothered with burden trouble
   ? cross seem heavy you are called carry
   Count your many blessings, every doubt will melt,
   And you will be singing as days go pass.

3. When you see others with their lands and gold,
   Think that Christ has promised you HIS riches not told;
   Count your many blessings, money can't buy
   Your reward[2] in heaven, or your home on high.

4. So, in middle trouble, no matter much or small,
   Don't become discouraged, God is over all;
   Count your many blessings, angels will come,
   Help and comfort give you to your traveling[3] end.

REFRAIN:

Count your blessings, name blessings one through one:
Count your blessings, See what God has done;
Count your blessings, name blessings one through one;
Count your many blessings, see what God has done.

Words, Johnson Oatman, Jr., 1897.

---

[1] You may make the sign for "feel blue" if you don't know the sign for "discourage."
[2] Make the sign for "gift."
[3] You may make the sign for "life's" in place of "traveling" if you feel that it gives more meaning

. Church's only foundation
Is Jesus Christ church's Lord;
Church is HIS new making,
Through Spirit and Word:
From heaven HE came and searched[1] church
For becoming HIS holy people,
With HIS blood HE bought church,
And for church's life HE died.

. Chosen from every nation,
Still one over all earth,
Church's true belief,
One Lord, one faith, one birth;
One holy name church blesses,
Take one holy food,
And to one hope church goes forward,
With every grace given.

. During work and trouble,
And noise from church's war (against evil),[2]
Church waits for coming
Peace forever more;
Until with sight glorious,
Church's wanting eyes are happy,
And great church victory
Shall become church at rest. Amen.

Words, Samuel J. Stone, 1866.

Make the sign for "seek" or "look," using the right "C" hand in front of the face.
Don't sign "against evil."

109   I Love Thy Kingdom, Lord

1. I love YOUR kingdom, Lord,
   House YOURS live-continue,
   Church our wonderful Redeemer[1] saved
   With HIS sweet, important blood.

2. I love YOUR church, O God!
   Church's walls before[2] YOU stand,
   Sweet same apple before YOUR eye,
   And carved on YOUR hand.

3. For church my tears shall fall;
   For church my prayers offer,
   To church my troubles and work are[3] given,
   Until works and troubles shall end.

4. More than my highest joy[4]
   I value church's heavenly ways,
   Church's sweet fellowship, true promises,
   Church's song with love and praise.

5. Sure same YOUR truth shall last,[5]
   To church shall be given
   Brightest glory earth can give,
   And brighter joy from heaven.

Words, Timothy Dwight, 1801.

---

[1] Make the sign for "Savior" with both "R" hands. You may just make a sign for "Savior."
[2] Make the sign for "presence."
[3] Make the sign for "truly."
[4] Make the sign for "happy" with one or both hands.
[5] Make the sign for "continue" instead of "last," if you prefer.

Baptist, 1975—240   Baptist, 1956—382   Broadman—19(

. Wonderful fellowship, wonderful joy[1] divine,[2]
Depending on everlasting[3] arms;
Wonderful blessing, wonderful peace is[4] mine,
Depending on everlasting arms.

. Oh, truly sweet walk in this ~~earthly~~[5] *Christian* way,
Depending on everlasting arms;
Oh, truly bright path[6] grows from day to day,
Depending on everlasting arms.

. What have I "push away," what have I fear,
Depending on everlasting arms?
I have wonderful peace with my Lord very near,
Depending on everlasting arms.

REFRAIN:

Depending, depending,
Safe and protected from all dangers;
Depending, depending,
Depending on everlasting arms.

Words, Elisha A. Hoffman, 1887.

Make the sign for "happy" with one or both hands.
Make the sign for "holy" with the right "D" hand, palm facing downward.
Make the sign for "forever." You can make the sign for "forever" with the right "E" hand moving in a clockwise circle and then forward with the hand in the "Y" position.
Make the sign for "truly."
You may sign "Christian" in place of "earthly."
Make the sign for "way." You may make the sign "way" with both "P" hands.

1. Blessed is[1] fellowship that joins
   Our hearts in Christian love;
   Fellowship same minds
   Is same that above.

2. Before[2] our Father's throne
   We make our true prayers;
   Our fears, our hopes, our aims are one,
   Our comforts and our troubles.

3. We share our same troubles,
   Our same burdens carry;
   And often for each other fall
   Tears[3] with feeling.

4. When we separate,
   That gives us inside pain;
   But we shall still be joined in heart,
   And hope meet again. Amen.

Words, John Fawcett, 1782.

---

[1] Make the sign for "truly."
[2] Make the sign for "presence."
[3] Make the sign for "falling tears" or "weeping tears." Make the sign for "cry" instead of "falling tears," if you wish.

Make Me a Channel of Blessing

1. Is[1] your life way for blessing?
   Is love HIS God showing through you?
   Are you telling lost people about Savior?
   Are you ready HIS work do?

2. Is your life way for blessing?
   Are you burdened for people lost in sin?
   Have[2] you urged[3] people who stray
   Accept Savior who died on cross?

3. Is your life way for blessing?
   Is your life daily telling for HIM?
   Have you spoken word about salvation
   To people who are dying in sin?

REFRAIN:

Make me way for blessing today,
Make me way for blessing, I pray;
My life controlling, my service blessing,
Make me way for blessing today.

Words, Harper G. Smyth, 1903.

[1] Make the sign for "truly."
[2] Make the sign for "finish."
[3] Make the sign for "beg" if you don't know the sign for "urge."

1. O Spirit from living God,
   YOU light and fire divine,
   Come down on YOUR church once more,
   And make church truly YOURS!
   Fill church with love and joy and power,
   With righteousness and peace,
   Until Christ shall live in people's hearts,
   And sin and sorrow stop.

2. Come, Spirit[1] from God! With wisdom[2] give
   Until our minds are free
   From ways of wrong, actions showing[3] doubt,
   That blind our eyes to YOU!
   Burn, Spirit[4] fire! Inspire[5] our lips
   With burning love and zeal,[6]
   Preach to all YOUR great good news,
   God's glorious people's good!

3. Teach us speak living words
   About truth that all can hear,
   Language all men understand
   When love speaks loud and clear;
   Until every age and group and place
   Shall blend[7] their beliefs in one,
   And earth shall make[8] one brotherhood[9]
   Through whom YOUR want is done.

4. Truly shall we know power HIS Jesus
   Who came people save.
   Truly shall we rise with HIM to life
   That goes beyond grave;
   And earth shall win true holiness,[10]
   That makes YOUR children holy,
   Until, perfected through YOU, we reach
   Creation's[11] glorious purpose![12] Amen.

Words, Henry H. Tweedy, 1935.

---

[1] Make the signs for "Blow, Wind" instead of "Come, Spirit" if you wish.

Make the sign for "wise."
Make the sign for "clouds of" instead of "actions showing" if you want.
You may make the sign for "wing" in place of "Spirit."
Touch the chest area with flattened "O" hands, palms facing self. Then, spread both hands upward.
Make the sign for "willing" or "enthusiasm."
Make the sign for "gear."
Make the sign for "establish" or "form."
Make the sign for "brother," ending with sign for "cooperate."
Make the sign for "holy" or "holy way."
Make the sign for "make." Make sign for "earth's" or "God's" instead of "creation's," if you want.
Make sign for "aim" or "goal."

We Gather Together   114

We meet[1] together ask Lord's blessing,
HE punishes[2] and hurries HIS will make known;
Sinful people persecuting[3] now stop from bothering,
Sing praises to HIS name, HE forgets not HIS people.

Near us guide us, our God with us joining,
Making, keeping HIS kingdom divine;[4]
Really from beginning fight we were[5] winning,
YOU, Lord, were at our side: glory be YOURS!

We all really honor YOU, YOU leader in war,
And pray that YOU still our defender[6] will be.
Let YOUR people escape trouble;
YOUR name be always praised: O Lord, make us free! Amen.

ords, Anonymous Dutch Hymn, 16th Century; translated, Theodore Baker, 1894.

Make the sign for "gather" instead of "meet," if you prefer.
Make the sign for "whip" if you like this better than "punishes."
Make the sign for "tease" with the right hand and then with the left hand.
Make the sign for "holy" with the right "D" hand, palm facing downward, when using "divine."
Make the sign for "true" or "truly."
Make the sign for "protect," and then make the sign for "er" as in "teacher."

1. Majestic[1] sweetness[2] same crown
   On Savior's forehead;
   His head with bright glory crowned,
   His lips with grace speak,
   His lips with grace speak.

2. No person can with HIM compare,
   Among children of people;
   Prettier is[3] HE than all pretty angels
   Who fill heavenly host,[4]
   Who fill heavenly host.

3. HE saw me fall in deep trouble,
   And came to my salvation;
   For me HE accepted[5] shameful cross,
   And carried all my sins,[6]
   And carried all my sins.

4. To HIM I owe my life and breath,
   And all joys I have;
   He makes me win over death,
   And saves me from death,[7]
   And saves me from death. Amen.

Words, Samuel Stennett, 1787.

---

[1] Make the sign for "glory" with the right "M" hand, palm facing downward.
[2] Make the sign for "sweet."
[3] Make the sign for "truly."
[4] Make the sign for "class" at the eye or forehead level.
[5] Sign "carried," if you prefer.
[6] Sign "grief," if you prefer.
[7] Sign "grave" instead of "death," if you like.

. We have story tell to nations,
That shall change their hearts to right,
Story about truth and mercy,
Story about peace and light,
Story about peace and light.

. We have song give to nations,
That will lift their hearts to Lord,
Song that shall overcome evil,
And destroy spear and sword,
And destroy spear and sword.

. We have words give to nations,
That Lord who controls above
Has sent HIS Son for saving us,
And show us that God is love,
And show us that God is love.

. We have Savior show to nations,
Who path[1] sorrow had walked,
That all world's great people
Can know truth HIS God,
Can know truth HIS God.

REFRAIN:

For darkness[2] shall change to morning light,
And morning light to noonday bright,
And Christ's great[3] kingdom will come on earth,
That kingdom HIS love and light.

Words, H. Ernest Nichol, 1896.

Make the sign for "way" with both "P" hands. You can just make the sign for "way," if you wish.
Make the sign for "dark."
Make the sign for "wonderful," if you prefer.

1. Going to YOU, O Christ my Lord,
   Trusting only in YOUR sweet, important word,
   Let my humble prayer to YOU be[1] heard,
   And send great revival in my soul.

2. Send Holy Spirit now within,[2]
   Clean and remove[3] guilt[4] full sin;
   Let YOUR powerful[5] works join with grace start,
   Oh, send great revival in my soul.

3. Send great revival, Lord, in me,
   Help me that I can rejoice[6] in YOU;
   Give me strength for winning,
   And send great revival in my soul.

4. Help me go for YOU, loving Lord, today,
   To some lonely soul that goes astray;[7]
   Help me lead lost souls in heaven's way,
   Oh, send great revival in my soul.

REFRAIN:

   Send great revival in my soul,
   Send great revival in my soul,
   Let Holy Spirit come and take control,
   And send great revival in my soul.

Words, B. B. McKinney, 1925. Copyright 1925. Renewal 1952 Broadman Press. All rights reserved

[1] Make the sign for "truly."
[2] Make the sign for "inside" with the fingers and thumb of the left hand, palm facing self, touching the heart or chest area.
[3] Make the sign for "take away."
[4] Strike the heart area twice with the right "G" hand, palm facing left and slightly downward.
[5] Make the sign for "power" or "strong."
[6] Make the sign for "happy" with both hands.
[7] Make the sign for "stray."

. Send revival,[1] O Christ, my Lord,
Let that go over land and sea,
Send revival following to YOUR loving Word,
And let that begin in me.

. Send revival among YOUR people,
Help us turn from our sins,
Let us get nearer Father's throne,
Make us live again, we pray.

. Send revival to people in sin,
Help people, O Jesus, turn to YOU.
Let people new life in YOU begin,
Oh, give people victory.

. Send revival in every heart,
Bring world nearer, O Lord, to YOU,
Let YOUR salvation true joy[2] give,
And let that begin in me.

REFRAIN:

Lord, send revival,
Lord, send revival,
Lord, send revival,
And let that begin in me.

Words, B. B. McKinney, 1927. Copyright 1927. Renewal 1955 Broadman Press. All rights reserved.

Rotate both "R" hands, palms facing self and fingertips brushing the heart area lightly.
Make the sign for "happy" with one or both hands.

1. There shall be[1] showers[2] of blessing:
   This is promise of love;
   There shall be times made new,
   Sent from Savior above.

2. There shall be showers of blessing,
   Important inspiring[3] again;
   Over hills and valleys,
   Noise showing plenty rain.

3. There shall be showers of blessing:
   Send rain on us, O Lord;
   Give to us a new eagerness,[4]
   Come and now honor YOUR Word.

4. There shall be showers of blessing:
   Oh, that today rain might drop,
   Now same to God we are confessing,
   Now same on Jesus we call!

REFRAIN:

   Showers of blessing,
   Showers of blessing we need:
   Mercy-drops round us are falling,
   But for showers we pray.[5]

Words, Daniel W. Whittle, 1883.

---

[1] Make the sign for "truly."
[2] Make the sign for "rain."
[3] Place both flattened "O" hands on the chest, palms facing self. Then spread both hands as you move them upwardly across the chest.
[4] Make a sign for "enthusiasm" or "willing." Some may prefer new "life" instead of new "eagerness."
[5] Make the sign for "beg," if you prefer.

Truly very[1] sweet trust in Jesus,
And accept HIM at HIS word;
Exactly depend on HIS promise,
And know, "This says Lord."

O wonderfully[2] sweet trust in Jesus,
Exactly trust HIS cleaning blood;
And in easy faith wash[3] me
Under healing, cleaning blood!

Yes, truly sweet trust in Jesus,
Exactly from sin and self stop;
Exactly from Jesus easily taking[4]
Life and rest, and joy and peace.

I am[5] very happy I learned trust YOU,
Important Jesus, Savior, friend;
And I know that YOU are with me,
Will be with me to end.

REFRAIN:

Jesus, Jesus, truly I trust HIM!
Truly I proved HIM again and again!
Jesus, Jesus, important Jesus!
O for grace trust HIM more!

Words, Louisa M. R. Stead, c. 1882.

Sign "this truly" instead of "truly very," if you wish.
Make sign for "Wonderful." Sign "O truly" instead of "O wonderfully," if you prefer.
You may use the sign for "baptize" or "clean."
Make the sign for "accept," if you wish.
Make the sign for "truly."

1. We praise YOU, O God! for Son from YOUR love,
   For Jesus who died, and is[1] now gone above.

2. We praise YOU, O God! for YOUR Spirit-giving light,
   Who has[2] shown us our Savior and taken away our night[3] of sin

3. All glory and praise to Jesus that was crucified,
   Who had accepted all our sins and had made clean every sin.

4. Revive[4] us again; fill each heart with YOUR love;
   Let each soul be made new with Spirit from above.

REFRAIN:

   Hallelujah![5] YOURS glory, Hallelujah! Amen;
   Hallelujah! YOURS glory, Revive us again.

Words, William P. Mackey, 1863.

---

[1] Make the sign for "truly."
[2] Make the sign for "finish."
[3] Make the sign for "dark." If you like, you may sign "dark sin" instead of "night of sin."
[4] You may sign "make us live again." If you want to use the word "revive," you may make th sign for "life" with both "R" hands.
[5] Make the sign for "praise" + "victory." If you would rather use the new sign, you can si "H" + "praise" + "victory," using both hands all the way. When signing "victory," use th old basic sign similar to that for "celebrate."

Walk you in HIM, all earthly ways leaving,
HE opens way to pardon from all sin;
HE is[1] way, HIS promises keeping,
Walk you in HIM, and feel HIS power within.[2]

Walk you in HIM, HIS footsteps always follow
Where no matter steps lead, over mountain, sea, or sand;
Serve HIM today, HE knows what comes tomorrow,
Walk you in HIM, obey HIS great order.[3]

Walk you in HIM, your way will lead to others,
No hands but yours can do HIS work today;
Go near and far make all people brothers,
Walk you in HIM, along narrow way.

Walk you in HIM, you who want tell story,
Open your heart, receive HIS promise true;
Then tell world about Jesus and HIS glory,
Walk you in HIM, and HE will walk with you.

ords, Roy H. Corley, 1965. © Copyright 1965 Broadman Press. All rights reserved.

Make the sign for "true" or "truly."
Make the sign for "inside" near the heart or chest area.
Make the sign for "command," if you prefer.

123 Come, All Christians, Be Committed

1. Come, all Christians, give yourselves
   To service HIS Lord.
   Make your lives for HIM more perfect,
   Cooperate your hearts with one agreement.
   Come into HIS presence with joy,
   Each his holy promises make new,
   Turn away from sin and sadness,
   Be changed with life again new.

2. Your time and talents give,
   Both are gifts from God above,
   Be used through Christians freely
   Tell HIS wonderful love.
   Come again serve Savior,
   One-tenths and offerings with you bring.
   In your work with HIM find kindness,
   And with joy HIS praises sing.

3. God's order love each other
   Is required from every person.
   Showing mercy to brother
   Shows HIS redeeming plan.
   In loving pity HE has given
   HIS love that is divine;
   On cross sins were forgiven;
   Joy and peace are fully yours.

4. Come in praise and love-worship,
   All who on Jesus' name believe.
   Worship HIM with holy lives,
   Grace and love will you receive.
   For HIS grace give HIM glory,
   For Spirit and Word.
   And tell again gospel story
   Until all people HIS name have heard.

Words, Eva B. Lloyd, 1966. © Copyright 1966 Broadman Press. All rights reserved.

Baptist, 1975—362

Lead YOUR church, O God, our Father,
Come through church's life today;
Give feelings of work
In our hearts and minds, we pray.
Help us to again new ourselves
To way of life in YOU
That makes for our understanding
How YOUR truth can make people free.

Make YOUR church living witness
To power of church's Lord;
Send us to world around us
With YOUR spirit and YOUR Word:
To inside city trouble,
To outside city where people go,
To all people who need your message;
Help us, Lord, live for YOU.

Give to us feeling for people
That makes us see
That all people are YOUR making
And that helping people serves YOU.
Let us feel with real loving pity,
Needs of body, mind, and soul;
For these needs let us give people
Help that makes them free.

4. Challenge us, O God, our Father,
To works that must be done
For YOUR church find satisfaction
In way taught through YOUR Son.
With knowledge of our purpose,
With ourselves given to YOUR call,
Let us prepare time when
Jesus will control as Lord of all.

Words, Milburn Price, 1970. © Copyright 1971 Broadman Press. All rights reserved.

Baptist, 1975—269

1. Jesus shall rule[1] where no matter sun
   Shall continually[2] shine;
   HIS kingdom spreads from nation to nation,
   Until moons shall brighten[3] and darken[4] no more.

2. From north to south princes meet
   Give their honor at HIS feet;
   While western nations accept their Lord,
   And African groups listen to HIS word.

3. To HIM shall all prayers be[5] made,
   And all praises crown HIS head;
   HIS name same sweet perfume shall lift
   With every morning sacrifice.[6]

4. People and kingdoms of every language
   Live on HIS love with sweetest song,
   And baby voices shall tell
   Their growing-up blessings on HIS name. Amen.

Words, Isaac Watts, 1719.

---

[1] Make the sign for "control" or "manage."
[2] Make the sign for "continue."
[3] Make the sign for "bright." Make the sign for "shine," if you like.
[4] Make the sign for "dark."
[5] Make the sign for "truly."
[6] Put both "S" hands in front of you, palms facing up. Then, move both hands upward while changin
them into sign for "offer."

Baptist, 1975—282   Baptist, 1956—116   Broadman—15

Save lost (people),[1] Care for dying (people),
Save people in mercy from sin and death;
Weep for sinning one, Help people in sin,
Tell people about Jesus strong save.

No matter people don't care HIM, Still HE is[2] waiting,
Waiting sorrowing person accept;
Beg with sinners really, Beg with sinners kindly,
HE will forgive if sinners only believe.

Down in people's hearts, Crushed through Devil,
Feelings hidden that only grace can help;
Touched through loving heart, Felt through kindness,
Lives that are broken will sing once more.

Save lost (people), Duty requires that;
Strength for your work Lord will give;
Again to narrow way Patiently win lost sinners;
Tell wanderer[3] Savior has[4] died (for him).

REFRAIN:

Save lost (people), Care for dying (people);
Jesus is merciful, Jesus will save.

Words, Fanny J. Crosby, 1869.

Don't sign the word(s) in parentheses unless you wish to.
Make the sign for "truly."
Make the sign for "stray" ending with a sign for "er" as in "teacher."
Make the sign for "finish."

1. Christ was born in far land,
   Tell good news, tell good news;
   Lived on earth for good of people,
   Tell good news, tell good news.

2. Christ became man on earth,
   Tell good news, tell good news;
   Gave HIS life for man's second[1] birth,
   Tell good news, tell good news.

3. Christ arose and to heaven went,
   Tell good news, tell good news;
   All can follow who repent,[2]
   Tell good news, tell good news.

4. Christ still lives in world today,
   Tell good news, tell good news;
   Giving strength to all souls who pray,
   Tell good news, tell good news.

REFRAIN:

Tell good news, tell good news,
Tell good news that Christ has come;
Tell good news, tell good news,
Tell good news to everyone.

Words, Gene Bartlett, 1968. © Copyright 1968 Broadman Press. All rights reserved.

---

[1] Make the sign for "again" instead of "second," if you wish.
[2] Make the sign for "change" with both "R" hands near the heart area. Make the sign for "confess" instead of "repent," if you want.

1. Love HIS God is[1] wider than earth's wide spread,
   Truly deeper wider than sea.
   Love reaches to all people bring plentiful[2] life,
   Because God much loved world HIS only Son HE gave.

2. All people who have[3] trusted in God's only Son,
   And have this sweet love in their hearts,
   Seek ways make love known to all who need know
   That God much loved world HIS only Son HE gave.

3. We show love HIS God each day we live,
   Show Christ's presence in our lives;
   And truly Holy Spirit leads us day through day.
   Because God much loved world HIS only Son HE gave.

REFRAIN:

   Share HIS love through telling what Lord has done for you,
   Share HIS love through sharing your faith,
   And show world that Jesus Christ is real to you
   Every minute, every day.

Words, William J. Reynolds, 1972. © Copyright 1972 Broadman Press. All rights reserved.

Make the sign for "truly."
Make the sign for "plenty" or "forever."
Make the sign for "finish."

1. O God with[1] power, O Son with light,
   O Holy Spirit sweet,
   YOUR church spread until all shall stand
   At Jesus HIS nailed feet.
   Let all who once YOUR Son not accepted
   Rejoice see HIM now on throne;
   Still while one straying soul there be,
   Send me, O Lord, send me.

2. With holy fire my heart inspire[2]
   YOUR Spirit HIS word use;
   With borrowed power I will take YOUR light,
   Until darkness ruin be gone.
   If others stop count cost,
   Because fear earthly things lost,
   I will count all profit die for YOU;
   Send me, O Lord, send me.

3. O that in me my Lord can see
   Carrier[3] YOUR name;
   That men may see HIS love truly free
   From year to year same.
   Be this my forever song,
   HE took on HIMSELF my wrong,
   And shouted while facing mountain-cross,
   "Send me, O Lord, send me."

Words, Ross Coggins, 1956. © Copyright 1956 Broadman Press. All rights reserved.

[1] Make the sign for "of," if you want.
[2] Touch the chest area with the flat "O" hands, palms facing self. Then, spread both hands upward
[3] Make the sign for "carry," ending with the sign for "er" as in "teacher."

. While passing through this world full sin,
And other people your life shall see,
Be[1] clean and pure, in heart and action,
Let other people see Jesus in you.

. Your life same book before[2] their eyes,
People read your life again and again;
? your life shows people to heaven,
? other people see Jesus in you.

. Wonderful joy will happen end of life,
In pretty homes above sky,
Meeting some souls that you have[3] won;
Let other people see Jesus in you.

. Then live for Christ both day and night,
Continue faithful,[4] continue brave and true,
And lead lost people to life and light;
Let other people see Jesus in you.

REFRAIN:

Let other people see Jesus in you,
Let other people see Jesus in you;
Keep[5] telling story, continue faithful and true,
Let other people see Jesus in you.

Words, B. B. McKinney, 1922, 1924. Copyright 1924. Renewal 1952 Broadman Press. All rights reserved.

Make the sign for "truly."
Make the sign for "presence."
Make the sign for "finish."
You may make the sign for "regular" with both "F" hands.
Sign "continue" instead of "keep," if you prefer.

131 Lord, Lay Some Soul Upon My Heart

1. Lord, put some soul on my heart,
   And love that soul through me;
   And let me bravely do my part
   Win that soul for YOU.

2. Lord, lead me to some soul in sin,
   And give that I may become
   Filled with power and love win
   That soul, loving Lord, for YOU.

3. Win that soul for YOU alone
   Will become my continued prayer;
   That when I have[1] reached great white throne
   I will meet that loving soul there.

REFRAIN:

   Some soul for YOU, some soul for YOU,
   This is[2] my real prayer;
   Help me each day, on life's way,
   Win some soul for YOU.

Words, st. 1, Anonymous; st. 2, 3, Mack Weaver and B. B. McKinney, 1939. From *The Broadman Hymnal*. Copyright 1940. Renewal 1968 Broadman Press. All rights reserved.

[1] Make the sign for "finished."
[2] Make the sign for "truly."

O people HIS God, hurry, your work, high accepting,
Tell all world that God is[1] Light;
That HE who made all nations is not willing
One soul shall die, lost in darkness full sin.[2]

Look how many thousands still are there,
Slaved in dark prison full sin,
With none tell them about Savior's death,
Or about life HE died for people save.

Tell every people, language, and nation
That God, in whom people live and move, is Love:
Tell how HE came save lost sinners,
And died on earth that man can live above.

Give your children carry message[3] glorious;[4]
Give your riches hurry them on their way;
Give your soul for them in prayer victorious;[5]
And all you spend Jesus will again pay.

REFRAIN:

Tell happy story, story about peace,
Story about Jesus, salvation,[6] and freedom.

Words, Mary Ann Thomson, 1868.

Make the sign for "truly."
Make the sign for "dark night" instead of "dark full sin," if you prefer.
Make the sign for "story" in place of "message," if you prefer.
Make the sign for "glory."
Make the sign for "victory."
You can make the sign for salvation with both "R" hands when using "redemption."

133   New Life for You

1. Son from God, our Savior,
   Has power clean from sin,
   Make people pure and holy,
   Again new without, within.[1]

2. Salvation[2] is[3] completed[4]
   Through faith in Christ alone;
   HE is Word become flesh[5]
   In whom our God is known.

3. HIS love truly great, no limited,
   Is offered free to all
   Who come to HIM confessing
   And yielding[6] to HIS call.

4. Salvation calls for service,[7]
   Walk with Christ each day;
   Master[8] speaks to others
   As we HIS life show.

REFRAIN:

New life in Jesus,
New life in HIM;
Crown HIM Savior, Lord, and King,
Brings[9] new life for you.

Words, Edwin McNeely, 1958. © Copyright 1958 Broadman Press. All rights reserved.

---

[1] Make the sign for "inside" near your heart area.
[2] Make the sign for "salvation" with both "R" hands when using "redemption."
[3] Make the sign for "truly."
[4] Make the sign for "finish." Sign "full," if you want.
[5] Make the sign for "body." You may make the sign for "body" with both "F" hands, palms facing self.
[6] Make the sign for "give up" or "surrender."
[7] Make the sign for "work" in place of "service."
[8] Sign "Savior" if you do not know the sign for "Master."
[9] Sign "means" in place of "brings," if you prefer.

. There is[1] call coming across stormy wave,
"Send light! Send light!"
There are souls help, there are souls save,
Send light! Send light!

. We have[2] heard far call today,
"Send light! Send light!"
And gold offering at cross we put,
Send light! Send light!

. Let us pray that grace everywhere spread,
"Send light! Send light!"
And Christ same Spirit everywhere be found,
Send light! Send light!

. Let us not grow tired in work of love,
Send light! Send light!
Let us get souls for crown above,
Send light! Send light!

REFRAIN:

Send light! blessed gospel light;
Let that shine from shore to shore![3]
Send light! blessed gospel light;
Let that shine forevermore!

Words, Charles H. Gabriel, 1890.

Make the sign for "true" or "truly."
Make the sign for "finish."
Make the signs for "from nation to nation," if you want.

1. Let song go around earth,
   Jesus Christ is Lord!
   Sound HIS praise, tell HIS worth,
   Be HIS name love-worshiped;
   Every place and language
   Join wonderful, glorious[1] song!
   Let song go around earth,
   Jesus Christ is Lord! Christ is King!

2. Let song go around earth,
   Where summer smiles;[2]
   Let stories of holy song
   Spread from far islands;
   Into woods, dark and thick,
   Cold lands give again song.
   Let song go around earth,
   Where summer smiles.
   Christ is King!

3. Let song go around earth,
   Jesus Christ is King!
   With story about HIS worth
   Let all earth sing;
   HIM people[3] all love-worship
   Forever and forever.
   Let song go around earth,
   Jesus Christ is Lord!
   Christ is King!

Words, Sarah G. Stock, 1898.

---

[1] Make the sign for "glory."
[2] Make the signs for "Where sun shines" if you like this line better.
[3] Make the sign for "making" when using "creation."

. Teach me, O Lord, I pray,
   YOUR sweet, important truth divine;
   Lead me understand YOUR Word
   And make YOUR laws mine.
   Give YOUR wisdom,[1] Lord,
   Give light on my way.
   That I can know YOUR great love;
   Teach me, O Lord, I pray.

. Train[2] me, O Lord, I pray,
   In knowledge[3] and expertise;[4]
   O daily let me walk with YOU
   And do YOUR perfect want.
   Train YOU my heart and mind
   Serve YOU not ashamed,[5]
   At home or far, where Christ
   Has not been told.

. Use me, O Lord, I pray,
   Give YOUR light highest[6]
   To rich and poor, to high and low
   Of every group and place.
   O let YOUR real zeal[7]
   Burn continually in me,
   Until souls in sin everywhere
   Kneel and worship YOU.

Words, G. Kearnie Keegan, 1959. © Copyright 1959 Broadman Press. All rights reserved.

Make the sign for "wise."
Make the sign for "practice." You may make the sign for "practice" with the right "T" hand.
Make the sign for "know."
Make the sign for "expert," "skill," or "talent."
Make the signs for "without shame" instead of "not ashamed" if you wish.
Make the sign for "high" if you wish. You may make a sign for "bright" or "wonderful" if you like.
Make the sign for "willing," "enthusiasm," or "eager."

1. How you share love HIS Jesus with lonely man?
   How you tell hungry man about Bread giving life?
   How you tell thirsty man about Living Water HIS Lord?
   How you tell him about HIS Word?

2. How you tell dying man about forever[1] life?
   How you tell only[2] child about Father's love?
   How you tell man who is[3] poor about wonderful riches HIS Lord[
   How you tell him about HIS Word?

3. How you tell world[4] without love that God HIMSELF is love?
   How you help man who is lying[5] lift his eyes above?
   How you tell sick man about healing power HIS Lord?
   How you tell him about HIS Word?

REFRAIN:

People who know go to people who need know Jesus;
People who love go to people alone without Jesus;
Because there are people who need see, people who need love,
People who need know God's redeeming[6] love.
People who see go to others who are blind without Jesus,
And this is people to people, yes, people to people,
All sharing together God's love.

Words, William J. Reynolds, 1971. © Copyright 1971 Broadman Press. All rights reserved.

[1] Make the sign for "forever" with the right "E" hand when using "eternal."
[2] Make the sign for "no father-mother" when using "orphan."
[3] Make the sign for "true" or "truly."
[4] Make the sign for "people" instead of "world," if you want.
[5] Make the sign for "lay" or "lie down." Sign "man on ground lift his eyes above?" if you like.
[6] Make the sign for "saving" with both "R" hands when using "redeeming."

1. Lord, I want be[1] Christian In my heart, in my heart,
Lord, I want be Christian In my heart.
In my heart, In my heart,
Lord, I want be Christian In my heart.

2. Lord, I want be more loving In my heart, in my heart,
Lord, I want be more loving In my heart.
In my heart, In my heart,
Lord, I want be more loving In my heart.

3. Lord, I want be more holy In my heart, in my heart,
Lord, I want be more holy In my heart.
In my heart, In my heart.
Lord, I want be more holy In my heart.

4. Lord, I want be same Jesus In my heart, in my heart,
Lord, I want be same Jesus In my heart.
In my heart, In my heart,
Lord, I want be same Jesus In my heart.

Words, Traditional Negro Spiritual; adapted, John W. Work, Jr., and Frederick J. Work, 1907.

---

[1] Make the sign for "true" or "truly." In stanza 1 make sign for "continue," if you want. In stanzas 2, 3, 4, make sign for "become" if you like this better than "truly."

1. I am going on heavenly way,
   New high I am advancing[1] each day;[2]
   Still praying as I onward go,
   "Lord, put my feet on higher ground."

2. My heart has no want stay
   Where doubts appear and fears bother;
   No matter some people can live in fear or doubt,
   My prayer, my aim is higher ground.

3. I want live above world,
   No matter devil's temptations to me are given;[3]
   Because faith has received happy sound,
   That song of Christians[4] on higher ground.

4. I want climb highest mountain
   And see future glory bright;
   But still I will pray until heaven I have found,
   "Lord, lead me on to higher ground."

REFRAIN:

   Lord, lift me and let me stand,
   With faith, on heaven's land,
   Higher land than I have found;
   Lord, put my feet on higher ground.

Words, Johnson Oatman, Jr., 1892.

---

[1] Make sign for "moving forward." This may be done by putting the left open hand, palm facing self, a few inches away from the chest and then placing the right open hand, palm facing self, in front of the left hand. Immediately following the right hand, rotate the left and then the right hand forward as if gaining the ground inch by inch and foot by foot.
[2] Sign "Better life I am showing each day" instead of "New high I am advancing each day," if you prefer.
[3] You may sign "No matter devil's tempting me I often face." If you use this one, make the sign for "presence" when you come to the word "face."
[4] You may make the sign for "holy" with the right "S" hand, palm facing down, ending with the sign for "er." Sign "God's people" or "holy people," if you prefer.

1. Sweetly, Lord, have[1] we heard YOU calling,
"Come, follow ME!"
And we see where YOUR footsteps,
Lead us to YOU.

2. No matter footsteps lead over cold, dark mountains,
Seeking HIS sheep,
Or along near Siloam's[2] water,
Helping weak.

3. If footsteps lead through temple holy,
Preaching Word,
Or in homes of poor and humble,
Serving Lord.

4. Then finally, when on high HE sees us,
Our life[3] done,[4]
We will rest where steps HIS Jesus
End at HIS throne.

REFRAIN:

Footsteps HIS Jesus
That make pathway[5] shine;[6]
We will follow steps HIS Jesus
Where no matter steps go.

Words, Mary B. C. Slade, 1871.

Make the sign for "finish."
A record tells about the tunnel of water from Gihon to the pool of Siloam. Make the sign for either "tunnel" or "underground." Either of these two signs will be better than the sign for "inscription" or "record."
Make the sign for "trip" if you think the deaf worshipers understand the meaning of this term. You may make the sign for "finish."
Make the sign for "way." You may sign "way" with both "P" hands.
Make the sign for "glow" or "shine."

1. My heart looks in faith
   To Jesus divine;[1]
   HIS sweet, important blood flows
   For all sins mine.

2. My heart looks in hope
   To Son HIS God;
   HE saves me, HE leads me
   On road HE walked.

3. My heart looks in love
   To Jesus my friend;
   HE really my soul strengthen[2]
   And my life defend.[3]

4. Faith and hope and love,
   All to Christ I give;
   HIS soldier I will continue
   Truly long as I live.

Words, T. C. Chao, 1931; translated, Frank W. Price.

---

[1] If you wish, make the sign for "holy" with right "D" hand, palm facing down.
[2] Make the sign for "strength" or "make strong."
[3] Make the sign for "protect" or "save."

Baptist, 1975—332

1. More about Jesus will I know,[1]
   More about HIS grace to other people show;
   More about HIS saving fullness[2] see,
   More about HIS love who died for me.

2. More about Jesus let me learn,
   More about HIS holy want understand;
   Spirit from God, my teacher be,
   Showing things about Christ to me.

3. More about Jesus, in HIS Word,
   Having fellowship with my Lord;
   Seeing HIS truth in every sentence,
   Making each faithful[3] word mine.

4. More about Jesus on HIS throne,
   Riches in glory all HIS;
   More about HIS kingdom's sure growth;
   More about HIS coming, Prince HIS peace.

REFRAIN:

   More, more about Jesus,
   More, more about Jesus;
   More about HIS saving fullness see,
   More about HIS love who died for me.

Words, Eliza E. Hewitt, 1887.

---

[1] Sign "I want know," if you prefer.
[2] Make the sign for "full."
[3] Make the sign for "regular" with both "F" hands. You may use "true" in place of "faithful," if you wish.

1. Nearer, my God, to YOU,
   Nearer to YOU!
   No matter that be[1] cross
   That lifts me;
   Still all my song will continue,
   Nearer, my God, to YOU!
   Nearer, my God, to YOU,
   Nearer to YOU!

2. There let my way seem,
   Steps to heaven;
   All that YOU send me,
   In mercy given;
   Angels invite me
   Nearer, my God, to YOU!
   Nearer, my God, to YOU;
   Nearer to YOU!

3. Then during my waking thoughts
   Bright with YOUR praise,
   Out from my much sorrows
   Holy place I will make;
   So through my troubles become
   Nearer, my God, to YOU!
   Nearer, my God to YOU,
   Nearer to YOU!

Words, Sarah F. Adams, 1840.

---

[1] Make the sign for "truly."

. Wonderful satisfaction,[1] Jesus is[2] mine!
Oh, wonderful knowledge about future glory divine![3]
Child through salvation, bought through God,
Born with HIS Spirit, washed in HIS blood.

. Perfect submission,[4] perfect happiness,
Visions[5] full joy now open[6] before[7] my eyes:
Angels coming bring from above
Words about mercy, telling about love.

. Perfect submission, all now wonderful,[8]
I with my Savior am happy and blessed:
Watching and waiting, looking above,
Filled with HIS goodness, lost in HIS love.

REFRAIN:

This is my story, this is my song,
Praising my Savior all day;
This is my story, this is my song,
Praising my Savior all day.

Words, Fanny J. Crosby, 1873.

---

[1] You may make a sign for "promise," if you like it better.
[2] Make the sign for "truly."
[3] Make the sign for "holy" with the right "D" hand.
[4] You may make the sign for "give up" or "surrender," if you wish.
[5] Make the sign for "prophet" without the "er" sign.
[6] You may make the sign for "happen," if you wish.
[7] Make the sign for "presence."
[8] You may make the sign for "rest," if you prefer this one.

Baptist, 1975—334   Baptist, 1956—269   Broadman—120

145   Jesus Loves Me

1. Jesus loves me! this I know,
   Because Bible tells me truly;
   Little children truly HIS;
   Children are[1] weak, but HE is strong.

2. Jesus loves me! HE who died
   Heaven's doors open wide!
   HE will wash clean my sin,
   Let HIS little child come in.[2]

3. Jesus loves me! loves me still,
   No matter I am weak and sin-sick;
   From HIS shining throne on high,
   Comes watch me where I lie.[3]

4. Jesus loves me! HE will stay
   Close near me all way;
   If I love HIM when I die
   HE will take me home on high.

REFRAIN:

    Yes, Jesus loves me,
    Yes, Jesus loves me,
    Yes, Jesus loves me,
    Bible tells me truly,

Words, Anna B. Warner, 1860.

---

[1] Make the sign for "truly."
[2] Make the sign for "enter" or "go in."
[3] Make the sign for "lay down" or "lying (on bed)."

Standing on promise HIS Christ my King,
Through eternal[1] years let HIS praises sound;
Glory in highest, I will shout and sing,
Standing on promise HIS God.

Standing on promise that can't fail,
When awful storm of doubt and fear bother,
Through living word HIS God I shall succeed,
Standing on promise HIS God.

Standing on promise HIS Christ Lord,
Join to HIM eternally through love HIS God,[2]
Overcoming daily with Spirit HIS Word,
Standing on promise HIS God.

Standing on promise I can't fall,
Listening every minute to Spirit HIS call,
Resting in my Savior as my all in all.
Standing on promise HIS God.

REFRAIN:

Standing, standing,
Standing on promise HIS God my Savior;
Standing, standing,
I am[3] standing on promise HIS God.

Words, R. Kelso Carter, 1886.

---

[1] Make the sign for "forever" with the right "E" hand.
[2] Use "strong tie" instead of "HIS God," if you prefer.
[3] Make the sign for "truly."

147 The Solid Rock

1. My hope is[1] built on nothing less
   Than Jesus HIS blood and righteousness;[2]
   I cannot trust any other person,
   But only depend on Jesus HIS name.

2. When darkness[3] seems hide HIS face,
   I depend on HIS never failing[4] grace;
   In every high and troubled way,
   My life depends on Jesus.

3. HIS promise, HIS agreement, HIS blood
   Support me through hard life;
   When all around my soul gives up,
   HE then is all my hope and help.

4. When HE shall come with horn sound,
   Oh, let me in HIM be found;
   Full with HIS righteousness alone,
   Blameless[5] stand before[6] throne.

REFRAIN:

On Christ, hard Rock, I stand;
All other ground is sinking sand,
All other ground is sinking sand.

Words, Edward Mote, 1832.

[1] Make a sign for " truly."
[2] Make the sign for "all right" by moving the right "R" hand, palm facing left, across the left ope
upward palm. You may sign "right doing," instead.
[3] Make the sign for "dark."
[4] Make a sign for "never changing," if you wish.
[5] Make a sign for "blame" to be followed with the spreading out of both hands, palms facin
slightly upward. Another way is to make the signs for "without" + "blame."
[6] Make the sign for "presence."

Baptist, 1975—337   Baptist, 1956—283   Broadman—9

My Soul in Sad Exile

My soul in sad escape was[1] out on life's sea,
Truly burdened with sin and trouble,
Until I heard sweet voice telling "Make ME your choice,"
And I entered heaven with rest.

I surrendered[2] myself to HIS sweet hug,
And faith accepting HIS word,
My chains came off, and I got my soul safe:
Heaven with rest in my Lord.

Song from my soul, since Lord made me free,
Has[3] been old story truly wonderful,
About Jesus who will save who no matter want
Home in heaven with rest.

Oh, come to Savior, HE patiently waits
Save through HIS power divine;[4]
Come, put your soul in heaven with rest,
And say, "My loving Savior is mine."

REFRAIN:

I have put[5] my soul in heaven with rest,
I will sail wide sea no more;
Wind may sweep over stormy sea,
In Jesus I am safe forever.

Words, Henry L. Gilmour, 1890.

Make the sign for "truly."
Make the sign for "give up."
Make the sign for "finish."
Make the sign for "holy" with the right "D" hand, palm facing down.
Make the sign for "place" instead of "put," if you like.

1. When peace, as river, comes my way,
   When sorrows as ocean waves;
   No matter what happens, YOU have taught me say,
   Truly good[1], truly good with my soul.

2. No matter devil shall tempt, no matter troubles shall come,
   Let this blessed[2] promise comfort me,
   That Christ has looked on my weak life,
   And has given HIS blood for my soul.

3. My sin—oh, joy, this glorious thought:
   My sin not some, but all
   Is nailed[3] to cross and I burden sin no more,
   Praise Lord, praise Lord, O my soul!

4. And, Lord, hurry that day when faith shall become seen,
   Heaven shall open as door,
   Horn shall announce and Lord shall come,
   Then, all is good with my soul.

REFRAIN:

   Truly good with my soul,
   Truly good, truly good, with my soul.

Words, Horatio G. Spafford, 1873.

---

[1] You may sign "all right" instead of "good," if you wish.
[2] You may make the sign for "wonderful," if you like this better.
[3] Touch the left open palm with the fingertip of the right index finger. Then hit the left palm wi
the closed right hand, palm facing left and the edge of the closed little finger touching the le
palm.

Baptist, 1975—339   Baptist, 1956—265   Broadman—7

Lord is my shepherd, I will be satisfied,
HE makes me lie down
In growing[1] green; HE leads me
Quiet water near.

My soul HE really make new again
And me walk really make
Inside path join with righteousness
Even for HIS name's sake.[2]

Yes, no matter I walk in death's dark valley,
Still will I fear no trouble;[3]
Because YOU are with me, and YOUR rod
And staff me comfort continually.

My food YOU have given
In presence my enemy;
My head YOU really with oil anoint,
And my cup overflows.[4]

Goodness[5] and mercy all my life
Shall surely follow me,
And in God's house forever
My living place shall become. Amen.

Psalm 23. Metrical version from the *Scottish Psalter,* 1650.

You may make the sign for "fence."
You may make the sign for "purpose."
You may make the sign for "bad" or "evil."
Make the sign for "runneth over." It is the same sign for "overflows."
Make the sign for "good."

151   I Surrender All

1. All to Jesus I surrender,[1]
   All to HIM I freely give;
   I will always love and trust HIM,
   In HIS presence daily live.

2. All to Jesus I surrender,
   Make me, Savior, all YOURS;
   Let me feel Holy Spirit—
   Truly know that YOU are[2] mine.

3. All to Jesus I surrender,
   Lord, I give myself to YOU;
   Fill me with YOUR love and power,
   Let YOUR blessing come on me.

REFRAIN:

   I surrender all,
   I surrender all;
   All to YOU, my blessed[3] Savior,
   I surrender all.

Words, Judson W. Van DeVenter, 1896.

---

[1] Make the sign for "give up."
[2] Make the sign for "truly."
[3] Make the sign for "wonderful," if you prefer.

, I know not why God's wonderful grace
To me HE has made known,
Not why, not worthy, Christ in love
Saved[1] me for HIMSELF.

, I know not how this saving faith
To me HE really give,
Not how believing in HIS Word
Made[2] peace within[3] my heart.

. I know not how Spirit moves,
Proving people their sin,
Showing Jesus through Word,
Making faith in HIM.[4]

, I know not when my Lord may come,
At night or noonday bright,
Not if I walk valley with HIM,
Or meet HIM in air.

REFRAIN:

But "I know whom I have believed,
And am sure[5] that HE is able
Keep that which I have given to HIM
Until that day."

Words, Daniel W. Whittle, 1883.

You may make the sign for "saved" with both "R" hands for the word "redeemed."
You may make the sign for "Gave" instead of "Made."
Make the sign for "inside" near the heart area.
Make the sign for "Jesus" in place of "HIM," if you like.
Sign "And know for sure that HE is able," if you prefer.

1. Purer in heart, O God,
   Help me become;
   Let me[1] give my life
   Fully to YOU:
   Watch YOU my straying feet,
   Lead me with advice sweet;
   Purer in heart
   Help me become.

2. Purer in heart, O God,
   Help me become;
   Teach me do YOUR want
   Most lovingly:
   Continue YOU my friend and leader,
   Let me with YOU live-continue;
   Purer in heart
   Help me become.

3. Purer in heart, O God,
   Help me become;
   Until YOUR holy face
   One day I see:
   Keep me from secret sin,
   Control YOU my soul within;[2]
   Purer in heart
   Help me become. Amen.

Words, Fannie Estelle Davison, 1877.

---

[1] Make the signs for "may I" instead of "let me," if you want.
[2] Make the sign for "inside" near the heart or chest area.

Baptist, 1975—323   Baptist, 1956—369   Broadman—2'

Take my life, and let me become
Consecrated,[1] Lord, to YOU;
Take my hands and let me sign
At feeling YOUR love.

Take my feet, and let me walk-continue
Quick and beautiful for YOU;
Take my hands and let me sing
Always, only, for my King.

Take my money and my gold,
Not one penny will I hold;
Take my minutes and my days,
Let me continue always praising.

Take my want, and make that YOURS,
My want shall be[2] no longer[3] mine;
Take my heart, that becomes YOURS,
My heart shall become YOUR royal[4] throne.

EFRAIN:

Lord, I give my life to YOU,
YOURS forever more become;
Lord, I give my life to YOU,
YOURS forever more become.

Vords, Frances R. Havergal, 1874.

Place both "C" hands in front of you, palms facing up. Move both hands upward while changing them into the sign for "offer." Sign "useful" instead of "consecrated," if you prefer.
Make the sign for "truly."
Make the sign for "more" instead of "longer," if you like.
Make the sign for "King" with the right "R" hand, palm facing self.

1. Jesus, keep me near cross,
   There sweet, important blood,
   Free for all people, true healing blood,
   Flows from mountain-cross.

2. Near cross, my fearing soul,
   Love and mercy found me;
   There Jesus, Bright Morning Star,
   Gives HIS light around me.

3. Near cross! O Son from God,
   Bring picture cross before[1] me;
   Help me live each day
   With cross leading me.

4. Near cross! I continue watch wait,
   Hoping, trusting always,
   Until I arrive heaven,
   After death.[2]

REFRAIN:

   In cross, in cross
   Continue my glory always,
   Until my saved soul will find
   Rest in heaven.

Words, Fanny J. Crosby, 1869.

---

[1] Make the sign for "presence."
[2] Sign "heaven, after death" very slowly to keep in rhythm with the music.

I am YOURS, O Lord, I heard YOU say,
And YOU told YOUR love to me;
But I want rise in arms of faith,
And be closer pulled to YOU.

Consecrate[1] me now to YOUR service, Lord,
Through power of grace divine;
Let my soul look up with continued hope,
And my want truly becomes YOURS.

O pure joy of one hour
That before YOUR throne I receive;
When I kneel in prayer, and with YOU, my God,
I talk as friend with friend!

There is much love that I can't know
Until I go to heaven;
There is much joy that I can't get
Until I rest in peace with YOU.

REFRAIN:

Pull me nearer, nearer, blessed[2] Lord,
To cross where YOU have died;
Pull me nearer, nearer, nearer, blessed Lord,
To YOUR sweet, important bleeding[3] side.

Words, Fanny J. Crosby, 1875.

Place in front of you both "C" hands, palms facing upward. Move both hands upward while spreading them open as if making a sign for "offer." You may just sign "use," instead.
Make the sign for "wonderful," if you wish.
Make the sign for "blood."

1. There is[1] place for quiet rest,
   Near to heart HIS God,
   Place where sin can't bother,
   Near to heart HIS God.

2. There is place for comfort sweet,
   Near to heart HIS God,
   Place where we our Savior meet,
   Near to heart HIS God.

3. There is place for full freedom,
   Near to heart HIS God,
   Place where all is joy[2] and peace,
   Near to heart HIS God.

REFRAIN:

O Jesus, blessed[3] Redeemer,
Sent from heart HIS God,
Keep us who wait before[4] YOU,
Near to heart HIS God.

Words, Cleland B. McAfee, 1901.

---

[1] Make the sign for "truly."
[2] Make the sign for "happy" with one or both hands.
[3] Make the sign for "wonderful," if you prefer.
[4] Make the sign for "presence."

Baptist, 1975—354   Baptist, 1956—301   Broadman—27

Jesus is Savior and Lord of [1] my life,
My hope, my glory, my all;
Wonderful Master in joy and trouble,
On HIM you too can call.

Wonderful Redeemer, all glorious King,
Worthy respect I give;
Honor and praises I joyfully bring
To HIM Life, Way.

Will you give up your all to HIM now?
Follow HIS want and obey,
Crown HIM as Lord, before HIS throne bow;[2]
Give HIM your heart today.

REFRAIN:

Jesus is Lord of all, Jesus is Lord of all,
Lord controlling my thoughts
And my service[3] each day,
Jesus is Lord of all.

Words, LeRoy McClard, 1966. © Copyright 1966 Broadman Press. All rights reserved.

Make the sign for "over," if you want.
Make the sign for "humble," if you wish.
Make the sign for "action," if you want.

1. Speak to my heart, Lord Jesus,
   Speak that my soul can hear;
   Speak to my heart, Lord Jesus,
   Quiet every doubt and fear.

2. Speak to my heart, Lord Jesus,
   Wash clean me from every sin;
   Speak to my heart, Lord Jesus,
   Help me lost people win.

3. Speak to my heart, Lord Jesus,
   My heart is[1] no longer[2] mine;
   Speak to my heart, Lord Jesus.
   I will always be YOURS.

REFRAIN:

Speak to my heart, oh, speak to my heart,
Speak to my heart, I pray;
Surrender[3] and quiet, seeking[4] YOUR want,
Oh, speak to my heart today.

Words, B. B. McKinney, 1927. Copyright 1927 Robert H. Coleman. Renewal 1955 Broadman Press. All rights reserved.

---

[1] Make the sign for "truly."
[2] Make the sign for "more" instead of "longer," if you like.
[3] Make the sign for "give up."
[4] Make the sign for "search" or "look," using the "C" hand in front of the face.

Open my eyes that I can see
Pictures showing truth YOU have for me;
Put in my hands wonderful key
That will open, and let me free;
Quietly now I wait for YOU,
Ready, my God, YOUR want see;
Open my eyes, make clear to me,[1]
Spirit divine![2]

. Open my ears that I can hear
Voices of truth YOU make clear;
And while YOUR words come to my ear,
Everything false will disappear:[3]
Quietly now I wait for YOU,
Ready, my God, YOUR want see;
Open my ears, make clear to me,
Spirit divine!

. Open my mouth and let me tell
Gladly YOUR warm truth everywhere;
Open my heart, and let me prepare
Love with YOUR children now share;
Quietly now I wait for YOU,
Ready, my God, YOUR want see;
Open my heart, make clear to me,
Spirit divine!

Words, Clara H. Scott, 1895.

Make the signs for "teach me" or "show me" rather than "make clear to me," if you prefer.
Make the sign for "holy" with the right "D" hand.
Make the sign for "melt."

161 The Great Physician

1. Wonderful doctor now is[1] near,
   Understanding Jesus;
   He speaks sad heart cheer,[2]
   Oh! hear voice HIS Jesus.

2. Your many sins are all forgiven,
   Oh! hear voice HIS Jesus;
   Go your way in peace to heaven,
   And wear crown with Jesus.

3. All glory to dying Lamb![3]
   I now believe in Jesus;
   I love wonderful Savior's name,
   I love name HIS Jesus.

4. HIS name melts my guilt[4] and fear,
   No other name but Jesus;
   Oh! truly my soul enjoys hear
   Sweet name HIS Jesus.

REFRAIN:

Sweetest name in angel's song,
Sweetest name in people's language;
Sweetest song ever[5] sung,
Jesus, wonderful Jesus.

Words, William Hunter, 1859.

---

[1] Make a sign for "truly."
[2] Make the sign for "make happy," if you don't know the sign for "cheer."
[3] Lamb is one of many names for Jesus. Use "Jesus" or "Son HIS God" instead of "Lamb,"
   you like.
[4] Strike the heart area twice with right "G" hand, palm facing left and slightly downward.
[5] Sign "any time" or "always," if you prefer.

O God who gives us everything,
Who gives this life to me,
I come again praise YOUR name
And ask for light[1] see
Life that I must live today,
Person I must become;
Then help me, Lord, know my place
In God's world today.

O help me learn share my faith
With all people everywhere,
And give me strength go to others
Who need YOUR healing care:
Showing to all people on earth
Love that Christ gave me;
Then will I find, O Lord, my place
In God's world today.

O Lord, today I give himself,
And now I humbly pray
For faith and strength and Christian love
Follow in YOUR way,
And waiting not do YOUR want,
Serve all people (everywhere);[2]
Then giving up all, I find my place
In God's world today.

ords, Ed Seabough, 1966. © Copyright 1966 Broadman Press. All rights reserved.

Make the sign for "understanding," if you wish.
Omit "everywhere," if you wish.

1. "Take your cross and follow ME,"
   I heard my Master say;
   "I gave MY life for ransoming[1] you,
   Surrender[2] your all today."

2. HE pulled me closer to HIS side,
   I sought[3] HIS want know,
   And in that want I now live-continue,
   Where no matter HE leads, I will go.

3. That may be through dark way,
   Or through life's troubles,
   I take my cross and follow HIM,
   Where no matter HE leads me.

4. My heart, my life, my all I bring
   To Christ who loves me much;
   HE is[4] my Master, Lord, and King,
   Where no matter HE leads, I will go.

REFRAIN:

   Where no matter HE leads, I will go,
   Where no matter HE leads, I will go,
   I will follow my Christ who loves me much,
   Where no matter HE leads I will go.

Words, B. B. McKinney, 1936. Copyright 1936. © Renewed 1964 Broadman Press. All right reserved.

[1] You may make the sign for "save," "saving," or "salvation."
[2] Make the sign for "give up."
[3] Make the sign for "seek," "look," or "search."
[4] Make the sign for "truly."

Jesus calls us above noise
Of our life's awful, windy sea;
Day through day HIS sweet voice sounds,
Saying, "Christian, follow ME!"

Jesus calls us from worship
Of proud[1] world's gold things,
From each sin[2] that will keep us,
Saying, "Christian, love ME more."

In our joys[3] and sorrows,
Days during work and hours during comfort,
Still HE calls, in troubles and pleasures,
"Christian, love ME more than these."

Jesus calls us: through YOUR mercy,
Savior, may we hear YOUR call,[4]
Give our hearts to YOUR obedience,[5]
Serve and love YOU best of all!

Words, Cecil Frances Alexander, 1852.

Make the sign for "worth nothing" instead of "proud," if you want.
Make the sign for "idol." If you do not know it, sign "sin."
Make the sign for "happy" with one or both hands.
Make the signs for "let us" instead of "may we," if you wish.
Make the sign for "obey."

165   O Master, Let Me Walk with You

1. O Master,[1] let me walk with YOU
   In humble paths[2] of service free;
   Tell me YOUR secret, help me accept
   Heavy work, complaining trouble.

2. Help me slow heart move
   Through some clear, winning word of love;
   Teach me straying feet stay,
   And guide feet in heavenly way.

3. Teach me YOUR patience;[3] still with YOU
   In closer, loving fellowship,
   In work that keeps faith sweet and strong,
   In trust that wins over wrong.

4. In hope that sends shining light
   Far into future's wide way,
   In peace that only YOU can give,
   With YOU, O Master, let me live. Amen.

Words, Washington Gladden, 1879.

---

[1] Make the sign for "Savior" or "Lord" if you don't know the sign for "Master."
[2] Make the sign for "way" with both "P" hands.
[3] Touch the mouth or lips with the thumb of the right "A" hand, palm facing left. Then, mov
the right "A" hand slightly downward.

. I can hear my Savior calling,
I can hear my Savior calling,
I can hear my Savior calling,
"Take your cross and follow, follow ME."

. I will go with HIM through prayer area,[1]
I will go with HIM through prayer area,
I will go with HIM through prayer area,
I will go with HIM, with HIM all way.

. I will go with HIM through judgment,
I will go with HIM through judgment,
I will go with HIM through judgment,
I will go with HIM, with HIM all way.

. HE will give me grace and glory,
HE will give me grace and glory,
HE will give me grace and glory,
And go with me, with me all way.

REFRAIN:

Where HE leads me I will follow,
Where HE leads me I will follow,
Where HE leads me I will follow,
I will go with HIM, with HIM all way.

Words, E. W. Blandy, c. 1890.

The garden where Jesus prayed is called the Garden of Gethsemane. For this reason, sign "prayer area" or "place of prayer."

1. I need YOU every hour,
   Most kind Lord;
   No sweeter voice as YOURS
   Can peace give.

2. I need YOU every hour,
   Stay YOU near me;
   Temptations lose their power
   When YOU are[1] near.

3. I need YOU every hour,
   During joy or pain;
   Come quickly[2] and live-continue,
   Or life is worth nothing.

4. I need YOU every hour,
   Teach me YOUR want;
   YOUR promises truly wonderful
   In me fill.[3]

5. I need YOU every hour,
   Most Holy One;
   O make me YOURS truly,
   YOU blessed[4] Son.

REFRAIN:

   I need YOU, O I need YOU;
   Every hour I need YOU!
   O bless me now, my Savior,
   I come to YOU.

Words, Annie S. Hawks, 1872.

---

[1] Make the sign for "truly."
[2] Make the sign for "hurry."
[3] Sign "To me give" instead of "In me fill," if you prefer.
[4] Make the sign for "wonderful," if you prefer.

1. Have faith in God when your way is[1] lonely,
   HE sees and knows all way you have[2] walked;[3]
   Never alone are smallest HIS children;
   Have faith in God, have faith in God.

2. Have faith when your prayers are not answered,
   Your true prayer HE will never forget;
   Wait for Lord, trust HIS Word, and (be) patient,
   Have faith in God, HE will answer you.

3. Have faith in God during pain and sorrow,
   HIS heart is touched with your sorrow and sadness;[4]
   Put all your troubles and your burdens on HIM,
   And leave troubles there, oh, leave troubles there.

4. Have faith in God no matter all other fail around you;
   Have faith in God, HE gives for HIS children;
   HE can't fail no matter all kingdoms shall fall,
   HE rules, HE sits on HIS throne.

REFRAIN:

   Have faith in God, HE is on HIS throne;
   Have faith in God, HE watches over HIS children;
   HE can't fail, HE must succeed;
   Have faith in God, have faith in God.

Words, B. B. McKinney, 1934. Copyright 1934. Renewal 1962. Broadman Press. All rights reserved.

Make the sign for "truly."
Make the sign for "finish."
It really means "lived."
Make the sign for "sad."

169   Am I a Soldier of the Cross?

1. Am[1] I soldier of cross,
   Follower HIS Lamb,[2]
   And shall I fear accept HIS kingdom,[3]
   Or ashamed speak HIS name?

2. Must I be carried to heaven
   On flowery[4] bed of comfort,
   While others fought win prize[5]
   And sailed through bloody seas?

3. Are there no enemies for me face?[6]
   Must I not stop flood?[7]
   Is not this bad world friend to grace,
   Help me on[8] to God?

4. Sure I must fight if I will control;
   Increase my courage,[9] Lord!
   I will accept work, suffer pain,
   Supported through YOUR Word.

Words, Isaac Watts, *c.* 1724.

---

[1] Make the sign for "true" or "truly."
[2] Make the sign for "Jesus," if you wish.
[3] Make the sign for "salvation" or "life" instead of "kingdom," if you wish.
[4] Make the sign for "flower."
[5] Make the sign for "victory," if you want.
[6] Make the sign for "presence."
[7] "Flood" is an idea for evil or enemies of God coming against us. We live, act, and stand fo
truth and goodness so that evil may be stopped. We are in a fight against bad things and group
in this world.
[8] Make the sign for "forward" or "onward."
[9] Make the sign for "brave."

1. My faith looks up to YOU,
   YOU[1] Lamb on mountain-cross, Savior divine!
   Now hear me while I pray, Remove[2] all my sin guilt,[3]
   O let me from this day forward Become fully YOURS!

2. Let YOUR wonderful grace give
   Strength to my weak heart, My enthusiasm[4] inspire;[5]
   As YOU have died for me, O let my love to YOU,
   Pure, warm, and continually[6] become living fire!

3. While through life's dark way I walk,
   And sorrow around me spread, Continue YOU my leader;
   Make darkness change to brightness,[7] Wipe away sorrow's tears.
   Never let me stray from YOU.

4. When finish life's short dream,
   When death's cold, slow water flow[8] comes over me,
   Blessed Savior, then, in love, Fear and doubt remove;
   O carry me safe to heaven, Saved soul! Amen.

Words, Ray Palmer, 1830.

[1] You may make the sign for "Jesus" in place of "YOU."
[2] Make the sign for "take away."
[3] Strike twice the heart area with the right "G" hand, palm facing left and slightly downward.
[4] Make the sign for "eager" or "willing," rubbing both open palms together.
[5] Touch the chest area with both flattened "O" hands and then spread both hands upward.
[6] Make the sign for "continue."
[7] Make the sign for "bright," "light," or "clear."
[8] Make the sign for "river" without the "R's."

1. How strong foundation, you saints[1] HIS Lord,
   Is made for your faith in HIS wonderful Word!
   What more can HE say than to you HE has said,
   To you who for protection to Jesus go?

2. "Fear not, I am with you; O don't become troubled,[2]
   For I am your God, and will give you help;
   I will strengthen[3] you, help you, and make you stand,
   Hold you with MY perfect, powerful hand.

3. "When through awful temptations your way shall face,[4]
   MY grace, all enough, shall meet your need:
   Temptation shall not hurt you; I only plan
   Your sin make clean, and your life make holy.

4. "That soul that on Jesus has depended for spiritual rest
   I will not, I will not leave to his enemies;
   That soul, no matter all hell shall try to destroy,
   I will never, no, never, no, never leave alone!" Amen.

Words, John Rippon's *Selection of Hymns*, 1787.

---

[1] Make the sign for "people." If you like, you can make the sign for "holy" with the right "S" hand, palm facing down, ending with the sign for "er."
[2] Before you sing this song, tell the deaf that it is Jesus who says all the words in stanzas 2, 3, and 4.
[3] Make the sign for "strong power."
[4] Make the sign for "presence." You may make a sign for "go," if you wish.

Stand Up, Stand Up for Jesus

1. Stand up, stand up for Jesus, You soldiers HIS cross;
Lift high HIS royal[1] flag, That must not suffer loss:
From victory to victory HIS army will HE lead,
Until every enemy is destroyed, And Christ is Lord really.

2. Stand up, stand up for Jesus, Horn call obey;
Onward to strong fight, In this HIS glorious[2] day:
You who are men now serve HIM Against many enemies;
Let bravery[3] equal with danger, And strength[4] to strength oppose.[5]

3. Stand up, stand up for Jesus, Stand in HIS strength alone;
Your flesh[6] will fail you, You better not trust yourself:
Put on gospel coat,[7] Put on coat with prayer;
Where duty calls or danger, Never without protection there.

4. Stand up, stand up for Jesus, War will not continue long;
This day noise from battle,[8] Next victory song:
To any person that overcomes[9] Crown of life will be given;
That person, with King from glory, Shall control forever.

Words, George Duffield, Jr., 1858.

---

[1] Make the sign for "king" with the right "R" hand.
[2] Make the sign for "glory."
[3] Make the sign for "brave."
[4] Make the sign for "strong."
[5] Make the sign for "against."
[6] Make the sign for "life" or "body." You may make the sign for "body" with both "F" hands.
[7] This does not mean a real coat. It is just an idea that we use God's Word and prayer to protect us from the devil and temptation.
[8] Make the sign for "war."
[9] Make the sign for "beat" as in "beating another football team."

1. Onward, Christian soldiers, Marching as to war,
   With cross HIS Jesus Going on[1] before![2]
   Christ, royal[3] Master, Leads against enemy;
   Forward into battle, See HIS flag go!

2. At seeing victory Devil's army escapes;
   On, then, Christian soldiers, On to victory!
   Hell's foundation shakes At shout praise;
   Brothers, lift your voices, Loud your songs sing![4]

3. As strong army Moves church HIS God;
   Brothers, we walk Where saints[5] walked;
   We are[6] not separated; All one group we,
   One in hope and doctrine,[7] One in love.

4. Onward, then, you people, Join our happy group,
   Join with ours your singing in victorious[8] song;
   Glory, praise, and honor To Christ King;
   This through many years People and angels sing.

REFRAIN:

   Onward, Christian soldiers, Marching as to war,
   With cross of Jesus Going on before!

Words, Sabin Baring-Gould, 1864.

---

[1] Make the sign for "forward" or "onward."
[2] Make the sign for "presence."
[3] Make the sign for "king" with the right "R" hand, palm facing self.
[4] Use "Brothers, lift your hands, Big your songs sign!" if you prefer.
[5] Make the sign for "past Christians." You may make the sign for "holy" with the right "S" hand palm facing down, ending with the sign for "er."
[6] Make the sign for "truly."
[7] Make the sign for "teaching." You may make the sign for "teaching" with both "D" hands, palms facing each other.
[8] Make the sign for "victory."

Baptist, 1975—393   Baptist, 1956—412   Broadman—46

1. God, give us Christian homes!
   Homes where we love and teach Bible,
   Homes where we seek Master's[1] want,
   Homes filled with beauty YOUR love has made;
   God, give us Christian homes;
   God, give us Christian homes!

2. God, give us Christian homes!
   Homes where father is[2] true and strong,
   Homes that are free from wrong,
   Homes that are happy with love and song;
   God, give us Christian homes;
   God, give us Christian homes!

3. God, give us Christian homes!
   Homes where mother, in queenly way,
   Tries show others YOUR way is best,
   Homes where Lord is honored person;
   God, give us Christian homes;
   God, give us Christian homes!

4. God, give us Christian homes!
   Homes where children come know
   Christ in HIS beauty who loves children truly,
   Homes where altar[3] fire burns and shines;
   God, give us Christian homes;
   God, give us Christian homes!

Words, B. B. McKinney, 1949. Copyright 1949 Broadman Press. All rights reserved.

---

[1] Make the sign for "Savior" or "Lord" if you don't know the sign for "Master."
[2] Make the sign for "real" or "really."
[3] Touch both thumbs of the "A" hands, palms facing down. Move both "A" hands away from each other—right hand to the right and left hand to the left horizontally. Then, move both "A" hands down, palms facing each other.

Baptist, 1975—397   Baptist, 1956—377

1. Prayer is soul's real want,
   Not spoken or shown,
   Action of hidden[1] fire
   That trembles[2] in breast.[3]

2. Prayer is burden with breath,
   Falling[4] of tear,
   Looking up eye
   When none but God is near.

3. Prayer is easiest way for speaking
   That baby lips can try;
   Prayer is prettiest song that reaches
   God on high.

4. Prayer is Christian's important breath,
   Christian's real air,
   Christian's secret word at time of death:
   He enters heaven with prayer.

5. O YOU through whom we come to God,
   Life, Truth, Way,
   Path[5] of prayer YOURSELF had walked:
   O Lord, teach us how pray. Amen.

Words, James Montgomery, 1818.

---

[1] Make the sign for "hide."
[2] Shake both hands, palms facing self and the fingertips spreading and pointing downward, as if showing the hands shaking with fear, while moving both hands slightly forward.
[3] Make the sign for "chest."
[4] Touch the cheek areas near the eyes with the index fingertips of open, spread hands, palms facing self. Wiggle the fingers while moving both hands downward.
[5] Make the sign for "Way" with both "P" hands.

Baptist, 1975—400   Baptist, 1956—336   Broadman—264

. Teach me pray, Lord, teach me pray:
This is my heart-shout day to day;
I want know YOUR want and YOUR way;
Teach me pray, Lord, teach me pray.

. Power in prayer, Lord, power in prayer!
Here among earth's sin and sorrow and trouble,
Men[1] lost and dying, souls without hope;[2]
O give me power, power in prayer!

. My weak want, Lord, YOU can make new;
My sinful life YOU can change;
Fill me exactly now with power new;
Power pray and power do!

. Teach me pray, Lord, teach me pray:
YOU are my example day to day;
YOU are my safety, now and for always;
Teach me pray, Lord, teach me pray.

REFRAIN:

Living in YOU, Lord, and YOU in me,
Always live-continue, this is my prayer;
Give me YOUR power, full and free,
Power with men and power with YOU.

Words, Albert S. Reitz, Copyright 1925 A. S. Reitz. Renewal 1953 Broadman Press. All rights reserved.

---

[1] Make the sign for "people," if you want.
[2] Make the signs for "People lost and dying, souls in loss of hope," if you wish.

177   What a Friend We Have in Jesus

1. What[1] friend we have in Jesus,
   All our sins and griefs carry!
   What honor carry
   Everything to God in prayer!
   Oh, what peace we often lose,
   Oh, what[2] not needed pain we suffer,
   All because we don't carry
   Everything to God in prayer!

2. ? have we troubles and temptations.
   ? trouble anywhere.
   We should never become discouraged,[3]
   Take that to God in prayer:
   ? can we find friend truly faithful[4]
   Who will all our sorrows share.
   Jesus knows our every weakness,
   Take that to Lord in prayer.

3. ? we weak and heavy burdened,
   Bothered with much trouble.
   Sweet, important Savior, still our protector;
   Take that to Lord in prayer;
   ? your friends hate, leave you.
   Take that to Lord in prayer;
   In HIS arms HE will take and protect you;
   You will find comfort there.

Words, Joseph Scriven, 1855.

---

[1] Make the sign for "wonderful" instead of "what," if you like.
[2] Make the sign for "much" instead of "what," if you prefer.
[3] Touch your chest area with middle fingers of both hands, palms facing self. Then, move both hands down with the middle fingers still sliding down on the chest.
[4] You may make the sign for "regular" with both "F" hands.

Baptist, 1975—403   Baptist, 1956—328   Broadman—16(

Sweet hour during prayer, sweet hour during prayer,
That calls me from world of [1] trouble,
And invites me at my Father's throne,
Make all my wants and wishes known!
During times of trouble and grief,[2]
My soul has often found comfort,
And often escape devil's temptation
Through prayer's answer,[3] sweet hour during prayer.

Sweet hour during prayer, sweet hour during prayer,
True prayer shall my needs carry
To HIM, whose truth and faithfulness[4]
Meets waiting soul bless:
And since HE invites me seek HIS face,
Believe HIS Word, and trust HIS grace,
I will tell HIM my every trouble,
And wait for prayer time, sweet hour during prayer.

Sweet hour during prayer, sweet hour during prayer,
Let me prayer's[5] comfort share,
Until from mountain[6] pretty high,
I see my home and take my wings:
This earthly body I will drop, and go
Get forever[7] life;
And shout, while passing through air,
"Good-bye, good-bye, sweet hour during prayer!"

ords, William Walford, *c.* 1840.

---

ake the sign for "full with," if you wish.
ake the sign for "sorry" or "sorrow" if you don't know the sign for "grief."
ou may make signs for "Because you come again" instead of "Through prayer's answer."
ake the sign for "regular" with both "F" hands.
 you wish, make the sign for "YOUR," although the word refers to "prayer."
isgah (Deuteronomy 3:27)—famous for its location as an outlook point in Moab that commands
good view of all southeast Palestine.
ake the sign for "everlasting" by making a clockwise circular motion with the right "E" hand
nd then moving the right "Y" hand forward, the palm facing forward all the time, if you want.

We Are Called to Be God's People

1. We are[1] called become God's people,
   Showing through our lives HIS grace,
   One in heart and one in spirit,
   Proof showing hope for all people.
   Let us show how HE has changed us,
   And again made us as HIS people,
   Let us share our life together
   As we shall around HIS throne.

2. We are called become God's servants,
   Working in HIS world today;
   Taking HIS work on us,
   All HIS holy words obey.
   Let us rise, then, to HIS orders,
   Give[2] to HIM our all,
   That we may become faithful servants,
   Fast answer now HIS call.

3. We are called become God's prophets,
   Speaking men for truth and right;
   Standing strong for right judgment,
   Bringing sin into light.
   Let us seek courage[3] needed,
   Our high calling accepting,
   That people may know blessing
   Through doing HIS[4] God's want.

Words, Thomas A. Jackson, 1973. © Copyright 1975 Broadman Press. All rights reserved.

[1] Make the sign for "true" or "truly."
[2] Place both "D" hands, palms facing upward, in front of self. Move both hands upward wh
   changing them into the sign for "offer." This hand motion is used whenever "dedicate" is use
[3] Make the sign for "brave."
[4] Leave out the sign for "HIS," if you wish.

Are you tired, are you heavyhearted?[1]
Tell that to Jesus, tell that to Jesus;
Are you crying[2] over joys gone?
Tell that to Jesus alone.

Do tears fall from your cheeks[3] not-expected?
Tell that to Jesus, tell that to Jesus;
Have you sins that people don't know?[4]
Tell that to Jesus alone.

Do you fear coming sorrow?
Tell that to Jesus, tell that to Jesus;
Are you worried what will be tomorrow?
Tell that to Jesus alone.

Are you worried thinking about death?
Tell that to Jesus, tell that to Jesus;
For Christ's coming kingdom are you waiting?[5]
Tell that to Jesus alone.

REFRAIN:

Tell that to Jesus, tell that to Jesus,
HE is a friend that is well known;[6]
You have no other wonderful friend or brother,
Tell that to Jesus alone.

Words, Jeremiah E. Rankin, 1888.

Make the sign for "sad" if you like this better than "heavyhearted" or "brokenhearted."
Make the sign for "grieve" if you know it.
You can leave out "from your cheeks." Just sign "Really tears fall not-expected?"
You can sign "don't see," if you prefer.
Make the sign for "looking" instead of "waiting," if you prefer.
If you don't know the idiom for "well known," then sign "HE is friend that all knows."

1. Ready suffer grief [1] or pain,
   Ready stand judgment;
   Ready stay home and send
   Others, if HE sees best.

2. Ready go, ready carry,
   Ready watch and pray;
   Ready stand aside [2] and give,
   Until HE shall open way.

3. Ready speak, ready think,
   Ready with heart and mind;
   Ready stand where HE sees worth,
   Ready stand trouble.

4. Ready speak, ready warn,
   Ready for souls want;
   Ready in life, ready in death,
   Ready for HIS coming.

REFRAIN:

   Ready go, ready stay,
   Ready my place fill;
   Ready for service, low or great,
   Ready do HIS want.

Words, A. C. Palmer.

---

[1] Make the sign for "sorry" or "sorrow" if you don't know the sign for "grief."
[2] Place the fingertips of the right "V" hand, palm facing downward, on the left open upward palm. Then, move the right inverted "V" hand right from palm area to the finger area of the left open upward hand.

When we walk with Lord
In light from HIS word
Wonderful glory HE gives on our way!
Let us do HIS good want;
HE lives with us still,
And with all who will trust and obey.

Not one burden we carry,
Not one sorrow we share,
But our work HE really pays;
Not grief or loss,
Not frown or cross,
But is[1] happy if we trust and obey.

But we never can prove
Pleasure of HIS love
Until all on altar we put;
For blessing HE shows
And happiness HE gives
Are[1] for all who will trust and obey.

Then in fellowship sweet
We will sit at HIS feet
Then we will walk near HIM on way;
What HE says we will obey,
Where HE sends we will go;
Never fear, only trust and obey.

REFRAIN:

Trust and obey, because there is no other way
Become happy in Jesus, But[2] trust and obey.

Words, John H. Sammis, 1887.

---

[1] Make the sign for "truly."
[2] You may make the sign for "except," if you wish.

183 We Lift Our Hearts in Songs of Praise

1. We offer our hearts in songs with praise
   For all YOUR gifts very good,
   For life and love through all our lives,[1]
   For fellowship through prayer.
   We pray that we can always share
   YOUR blessings from heaven,
   Show people that we really care,
   And teach people about God's love.

2. To people who live in poverty,[2]
   In deep trouble and need,
   Let us show Christian kindness[3]
   In love and word and action.
   To people from every nation and language,
   Blind, deaf, crippled,
   To all lonely people, old, and young,
   We serve all people in Christ HIS name.

3. We will answer with love and interest
   To all people in sorrow,
   And with people hope and courage[4] share
   Strengthen[5] their faith.[6]
   Good news we will share with everyone—
   YOUR love at mountain-cross,
   In giving Christ, YOUR only Son,
   That all can come to YOU.

Words, Lilian Yarborough Leavell, 1969. © Copyright 1969 Broadman Press. All rights reserve

---

[1] Make the sign for "days," if you prefer.
[2] Make the sign for "poor."
[3] Make the sign for "kind.'
[4] Make the sign for "brave."
[5] Make the sign for "strength" or "make strong."
[6] Make the sign for "belief" instead of "faith," if you want.

"Serve Lord with gladness"[1] In our doings and ways,
Come into HIS presence With our songs praise;
To HIM our Maker We will pledge[2] again
Life's highest devotion[3] To service true.

"Serve Lord with gladness," Thankful all time[4]
For HIS wonderful mercies, For HIS loving smile:
Blessed truth continue, Always exact same,
We will serve with gladness And praise HIS name.

"Serve Lord with gladness," This shall become our theme,[5]
While we walk together In HIS love wonderful:[6]
Listen, always listen For soft, sweet voice,
HIS sweet want, sweet, important, Will become our choice.

EFRAIN:

"Serve HIM with gladness," Enter HIS presence with song;
To our Maker True praises give:
Wonderful is HIS mercy, Wonderful is HIS name,
We gladly serve HIM, HIS wonderful love announce.

ords, B. B. McKinney, 1930. Copyright 1931. Renewal 1959 Broadman Press. All rights reserved.

Make the sign for "happy" with one or both hands.
You may make the sign for "promise."
Make the sign for "gift" with both "D" hands, palms facing each other, and right "D" touching chest or heart area at the outset.
Make the sign for "time" (seasonal). Place the left flat hand in front of you, palm facing self and slightly upward. Now, place the right "T" hand above left palm. Then, move the right "T" hand in a clockwise circle over left palm, ending with a touch of right hand on left palm, both palms facing each other.
Make the sign for "quotation mark."
You may make the sign for "holy" with the right "D" hand.

1. I gave MY life for you,
   MY sweet, important blood I gave,
   That you can saved be,[1]
   And made alive from dead;
   I gave, I gave MY life for you,
   What have[2] you given for ME?
   I gave, I gave MY life for you,
   What have you given for ME?

2. MY Father's house bright,
   MY glory around throne,
   I left for earth's darkness,[3]
   For straying sad and lone;
   I left, I left that all for you,
   Have you left anything for ME?
   I left, I left that all for you,
   Have you left anything for ME?

3. I suffered much for you,
   More than you can tell,
   About bitter suffering,
   For saving you from hell;
   I have suffered, I have suffered that all for you,
   What have you suffered for ME?
   I have suffered, I have suffered that all for you,
   What have you suffered for ME?

4. And I have brought to you,
   Down from MY home above,
   Salvation full and free,
   My forgiveness[4] and MY love;
   I bring, I bring wonderful gifts to you,
   What have you brought to ME?
   I bring, I bring wonderful gifts to you,
   What have you brought to ME?

Words, Frances R. Havergal, 1858.

---

* Be sure to let the deaf people know that it is Jesus who says all the words to them in th
song.

Make the sign for "truly."
Make the sign for "finish."
Make the sign for "dark."
Make the sign for "forgive" or "pardon."

Baptist, 1975—417   Baptist, 1956—399   Broadman—222

Something for Thee   186

Savior, YOUR dying love YOU gave me,
Not want I something keep, Loving Lord, from YOU:
In love my soul will humble,[1] My heart keep promise,
Some offering bring YOU now, Something for YOU.

At wonderful mercy seat, Begging for me,
My weak faith looks up, Jesus, to YOU:
Help me cross carry, YOUR wonderful love tell,
Some song offer, or prayer, Something for YOU.

Give me true[2] heart, Same to YOU,
That each passing day From now on[3] can see
Some work with love begin, Some action kindness[4] done,[5]
Some person sought[6] and won, Something for YOU.

All that I am and have, YOUR gift truly free,
In joy, in sorrow, through life, Loving Lord, for YOU!
And when YOUR face I see, My saved soul shall become,
Through forever, Something for YOU. Amen.

Words, Sylvanus D. Phelps, 1864.

Make the sign for "bow," if you prefer.
Make the sign for "faithful" by using the sign for "regular" with both "F" hands, if you prefer.
Touch the back of the left open hand, palm facing self, with open palm of the right hand. Then, move the right hand forward. This is the sign for "henceforth" or "thereafter."
Make the sign for "kind."
Since "done" is a repetition of the sign for "action," you may use "shown" instead.
Make the sign for "seek" or "look."

Baptist, 1975—418   Baptist, 1956—400   Broadman—149

1. Jesus means all world to me,
   My life, my joy,[1] my all;
   HE is[2] my strength[3] from day to day,
   Without HIM I would fall:
   When I feel sad, to HIM I go,
   No other person can give me joy;
   When I feel sad HE makes me happy,
   HE is my friend.

2. Jesus means all world to me,
   My friend during trouble much;
   I go to HIM for blessings,
   And HE gives me blessing again and again:
   HE sends sunshine and rain,
   HE sends harvest's[4] golden growings;
   Sunshine and rain, harvest's growings,
   HE is my friend.

3. Jesus means all world to me,
   And true to HIM I will continue;
   Oh, how can I this friend deny,
   When HE is faithful to me?
   Following HIM I know I am right,
   HE watches over me day and night;
   Following HIM during day and night,
   HE is my friend.

4. Jesus means all world to me,
   I want no better friend;
   I trust HIM now, I will trust HIM when
   Life nears end:
   Beautiful life with wonderful friend,
   Beautiful life that has no end;
   Eternal[5] life, eternal joy,
   HE is my friend.

Words, Will L. Thompson, 1904.

---

[1] Make the sign for "happy" or "glad."

Make the sign for "truly."
Make the sign for "strong."
Make the sign for "collect."
Make the sign for "forever" with your right "E" hand.

Lead On, O King Eternal   188

Lead on, O King Eternal, Time[1] for march has come;
Now on[2] in field overcoming[3] YOUR places[4] shall be our home:
Through days preparing YOUR grace has made us strong,
And now, O King Eternal, We offer our war song.

Lead on, O King Eternal, Until sin's awful war shall stop,
And holiness shall tell Sweet amen[5] of peace;
For not with swords loud sounding Or noise from beating drums;[6]
With actions showing love and mercy Heavenly kingdom comes.

Lead on, O King Eternal, We follow, not with fears;
Because gladness comes as morning Where YOUR face appears;
YOUR cross is lifted above us; We go in cross's light:
Crown waits winner; Lead on, O God with power.

Words, Ernest W. Shurtleff, 1887.

Make the sign for "day" instead of "time," if you prefer.
Place the left open hand, palm facing self, near your chest area. Touch the back of the left hand with palm of the right hand. Move the right hand forward.
Make the sign for "beat," moving the right hand over the left wrist. Make the sign for "capture" you like this better.
Make the sign for "tent," if you wish.
Make the sign for "prayer," if you want.
Make the sign for "vibrating drums" instead of "beating drums" if you prefer to sign "vibrate." Shake the right hand to the right and the left hand to the left, both palms facing down. If you don't know how to sign "vibrating drums," stay with "beating drums."

1. Truly never day sad,
   Truly never night long,
   But that soul trusting Jesus
   Will somewhere find song.

2. Truly never cross heavy,
   Truly never heavy burden,
   But Jesus will help us carry
   Because HE loves us truly.

3. Truly never trouble or burden,
   Truly never grief or loss,
   But Jesus in love will make easy
   When carried to cross.

4. Truly never guilty[1] sinner,
   Truly never stray person,
   But God can in mercy forgive
   Through Jesus Christ, HIS Son.

REFRAIN:

   Wonderful, wonderful Jesus,
   In heart HE started song;
   Song about salvation, about courage,[2] about strength;[3]
   In heart HE started song.

Words, Anna B. Russell, 1921.

---

[1] Strike the heart area twice with the right "G" hand, palm facing left and downward.
[2] Make the sign for "brave."
[3] Make the sign for "strong."

God moves in strange way
HIS wonders[1] do;
HE shows HIS footsteps in sea,
And goes through storm.

You fearing Christians, new courage[2] accept;
Clouds you very much afraid
Really much with mercy, and shall come
With blessing on you.

Don't judge Lord through weak feeling,
But trust HIM for HIS grace;
Behind frowning[3] action
God hides smiling face.

Blind not-belief is[4] sure fail,
And look for God's work without success,
God is HIS interpreter HIMSELF,
And HE will make everything clear. Amen.

ords, William Cowper, 1774.

Make the sign for "wonderful."
Make the sign for "brave."
Make the sign for "angry" or "mad" with the right hand in front of the face.
Make the sign for "truly."

191   He Keeps Me Singing

1. Here is within my heart song;
   Jesus says sweet and easy,[1]
   "Fear not, I am with you, peace, be quiet,"
   During all my life's going and coming.

2. All my life was ruined through sin and trouble,
   Confusion[2] filled my heart with pain,
   Jesus came across my broken life,
   Started my life sing again.

3. Living on kindness HIS grace,
   Resting under HIS protecting arm,
   Always looking on HIS smiling face,
   That is why I shout and sing.

4. No matter sometimes HE leads me through trouble,
   Temptations come my way,
   No matter way seems rough and hard,
   See HIS footsteps all way.

5. Soon HE is coming again welcome me
   Far above starry sky;
   I shall fly to worlds not known,
   I shall live with HIM on high.

REFRAIN:

    Jesus, Jesus, Jesus,
    Sweetest name I know,
    Fills my every wanting,
    Keeps me singing while[3] I go.

Words, Luther B. Bridgers, 1910. Copyright 1910. Renewal 1937 Broadman Press. All right reserved.

---

[1] Use the sign for "kind" or "soft," if you prefer.
[2] Make the sign for "mix up" or "mix" if you like this one better.
[3] Make the sign for "as," if you like.

Baptist, 1975—435   Baptist, 1956—307   Broadman—39

. Tell me story about Jesus,
Write on my heart each word;
Tell me that story most sweet, important,
Sweetest since I heard.
Tell how angels, in group,[1]
Sang while welcoming Jesus' birth,
"Glory to God in highest!
Peace and good news to earth."

. Fasting[2] alone in lonely place,
Tell me about days past,[3]
How for our sins Jesus met temptation,
Still won at last.[4]
Tell about years during HIS hard work,
Tell about sorrow HE accepted,
Jesus was hated and persecuted,
Without home, alone, and poor.

. Tell about that cross where soldiers nailed[5] HIM,
Suffering awful pain;
Tell about grave where soldiers put Jesus,
Tell how HE lives again.
Love in that story truly soft-kind,
More clear than before I see:
Stay, let me cry while you tell me,
Love paid sin debt for me.

EFRAIN:

Tell me story about Jesus,
Write on my heart each word;
Tell me story most sweet, important,
Sweetest since I heard.

'ords, Fanny J. Crosby, 1880.

Make the sign for "class."
Move the right "F" hand, palm facing self, across the lips from the left to the right.
Make the sign for "past." You may sign "long ago."
Make the sign for "final."
You may make the sign for "crucify."

1. Easy trusting every day,
   Trusting through life's way;
   Even when my faith is small,
   Trusting Jesus, that is all.

2. Brightly HIS Spirit shine
   Into this poor heart mine;
   While HE leads I cannot fall;
   Trusting Jesus, that is all.

3. Singing if my way is clear,
   Praying if way be sad;[1]
   If in danger, for HIM call;
   Trusting Jesus, that is all.

4. Trusting HIM while life shall continue,
   Trusting HIM until earth be gone;[2]
   Until within[3] heavenly room,
   Trusting Jesus, that is all.

REFRAIN:

   Trusting as minutes pass,
   Trusting as days go pass;
   Trusting HIM what no matter happens,
   Trusting Jesus, that is all.

Words, Edgar Page Stites, 1876.

---

[1] Make the sign for "dark" instead of "sad," if you prefer.
[2] Make the sign for "gone" in an idiomatic way, if you know one. Make the signs for "Trust
   HIM until I leave earth," if you prefer.
[3] Make the sign for "inside."

I have song I love sing,
Since I have become redeemed,[1]
About my Redeemer, Savior, and King,
Since I have become redeemed.

I have Jesus who satisfies,
Since I have become redeemed,
Obey HIS want my highest honor,
Since I have become redeemed.

I have witness bright very clear,
Since I have become redeemed,
Melting every doubt and fear,
Since I have become redeemed.

I have home prepared for me,
Since I have become redeemed,
Where I shall live eternally,[2]
Since I have become redeemed.

REFRAIN:

Since I have become redeemed,
Since I have become redeemed,
I will glory in HIS name;
Since I have become redeemed,
I will glory in my Savior's name.

Words, Edwin O. Excell, 1884.

---

[1] Make the sign for "saved." You can make a sign for "saved" with both "R" hands if you want to use "redeemed."
[2] Make the sign for "forever."

195 Redeemed, How I Love to Proclaim It

1. Redeemed,[1] truly I love announce[2] that!
   Redeemed through blood from Jesus;
   Redeemed through HIS infinite[3] mercy,
   HIS child forever I am.

2. Redeemed, truly happy in Jesus,
   No language my joy can tell;
   I know that light in HIS presence
   With me continually[4] lives.

3. I think about my wonderful Redeemer,
   I think about Jesus all day;
   I sing because I can't keep quiet;
   HIS love is theme[5] for my song.

4. I know I will see in HIS beauty
   That King in HIS law I enjoy;[6]
   Who kindly protects my walking
   And gives me songs during night.

REFRAIN:

   Redeemed, redeemed,
   Redeemed with blood from Jesus;
   Redeemed, redeemed,
   HIS child forever I am.

Words, Fanny J. Crosby, 1882.

---

[1] Make the sign for "saved." You can make the sign for "saved" with both "R" hands. For "Redeemer," add the sign "er."
[2] You may make the sign for "tell."
[3] You may make the sign for "great," "large," or "much."
[4] Make the sign for "continue."
[5] Make the sign for "quotation mark."
[6] Make the sign for "pleasure."

. On earth's stormy shore I stand,
And look with wanting eye
To heaven's beautiful and happy land,
Where my things are.[1]

. All over wide spread land
Shines one forever[2] day;
There God Son forever controls
And takes away night.

. No cold wind, no poisonous[3] breath
Can touch healthful[4] shore;
Sickness[5] and sorrow, pain and death
Are felt and feared no more.

. When shall I reach that happy place,
And be forever happy?
When shall I see my Father's face,
And in HIS breast rest?

REFRAIN:

I am going for promised land,
I am going for promised land;
O who will come and go with me?
I am going for promised land.

Words, Samuel Stennett, 1787.

Make the sign for "truly."
Make the sign for "forever" with the right "E" hand when using "eternal," if you prefer.
Make the sign for "poison."
Make the sign for "health."
Make the sign for "sick."

1. Wonderful Savior is Jesus my Lord,
   Wonderful Savior to me;
   HE hides my soul in hole[1] of rock,
   Where rivers with pleasure[2] I see.

2. Wonderful Savior is Jesus my Lord,
   HE takes my burden away;
   HE helps me stand, and I shall not fall,[3]
   HE gives me strength as my day.

3. With many blessings each minute HE crowns,[4]
   And filled with HIS fulness[5] divine,
   I sing in my joy, Oh, glory to God
   For wonderful Redeemer as mine!

4. When clothed in brightness,[6] carried I go
   Meet HIM in clouds in sky,
   HIS perfect salvation, HIS wonderful love
   I will shout with millions on high.

REFRAIN:

   HE hides my soul in hole of rock
   That black-shapes[7] dry thirsty land;
   HE hides my life in deep HIS love,
   And covers[8] me there with HIS hand,
   And covers me there with HIS hand,

Words, Fanny J. Crosby, 1890.

---

[1] Make the sign for "opening" instead of "hole," if you want.
[2] Make the sign for "enjoy" with both hands.
[3] The line really means that "Jesus holds me up, and I shall not be moved or pushed by anythi⬤
or any person."
[4] Make the sign for "give" in place of "crown," if you want.
[5] Make the sign for "full" or "fill."
[6] Make the sign for "bright."
[7] Make the sign for "cools" instead of "black-shape" or "shadows," if you wish.
[8] Make the sign for "hide" in place of "covers," if you want.

Baptist, 1975—451   Baptist, 1956—272

. Very important is Jesus, my Savior, my King,
HIS praise all day long with happiness I sing;
To HIM is my weakness[1] for strength I can hold,
For[2] HE is very important to me.

. HE stood at my heart's door in sunshine and rain,
And patiently waited entrance[3] live;[4]
Awful shame that very long HE begged without success,
For HE is very important to me.

. I stand on mountain of blessing finally,
No cloud in heaven black shape is seen;
HIS smile is on me, valley is past,[5]
For HE is very important to me.

. I praise HIM because HE chose place
Where, someday, through faith in HIS wonderful grace,
I know I shall see HIM, shall look on HIS face,
For HE is very important to me.

REFRAIN:

For HE is very important to me,
For HE is very important to me,
Truly heaven on earth my Redeemer[6] know,
For HE is very important to me.

Words, Charles H. Gabriel, 1902.

Make the sign for "weak."
Sign "because" if you like this one better.
Make the sign for "enter."
You may make the sign for "success" instead of "live." The sign "enter-success" is an idiomatic expression of many deaf people.
Make the sign for "pass."
Make the sign for "Savior." You may make a sign for "Savior" with both "R" hands.

199 Love Is the Theme

1. About[1] themes[2] that people have known,
   One highly stands alone;
   Through years that has shown,
   This HIS wonderful, wonderful love.

2. Let bells in heaven ring,
   Let saints[3] their honor bring,
   Let world true praises sing
   About HIS wonderful, wonderful love.

3. Since Lord my soul saved,
   I am telling all around me,
   Forgiveness,[4] peace, and joy are found
   In HIS wonderful, wonderful love.

4. As in long ago[5] when blind and crippled
   To blessed Master went,
   Sinners, call you on HIS name,
   Trust HIS wonderful, wonderful love.

REFRAIN:

   Love is theme, love is highest above all;
   Sweeter love grows, glory gives;
   Bright as sun always love shines!
   Love is theme, eternal theme!

Words, Albert C. Fisher, 1912. Copyright 1912. Renewal 1940, Robert H. Coleman. Broadman Press, owner. All rights reserved.

---

[1] You may make the sign for "among," if you like.
[2] Make the sign for "quotation mark."
[3] You may make the sign for "Christians" or "God's people." If you wish, you can make the sign for "holy" with the right "S" hand, palm facing downward, ending with the "er" sign.
[4] Make the sign for "forgive" or "pardon."
[5] You may make signs for "long time ago," if you prefer.

Down at the Cross

200

. There on cross my Savior died,
There for cleansing from sin I prayed,
There to my heart was[1] HIS blood given;
Glory to HIS name.

2. I am wonderfully saved from sin,
Jesus truly sweetly lives within;[2]
There on cross Jesus accepted me;
Glory to HIS name.

3. Oh, sweet, important blood that saves me from sin,
I am very happy I accepted HIM;
There Jesus saved me and keeps me clean;
Glory to HIS name.

4. Come to Jesus' blood truly wonderful and sweet;
Confess your sins to Jesus;
Accept Jesus now, and become full new;
Glory to HIS name.

REFRAIN:

Glory to HIS name,
Glory to HIS name:
There to my heart was HIS blood given;
Glory to HIS name.

Words, Elisha A. Hoffman, 1878.

Make the sign for "truly."
Make the sign for "inside," having the fingers of the left hand, palm facing self, touching the heart area.

1. I am satisfied with Jesus,
   HE has done much for me:
   HE has suffered for redeeming[1] me,
   HE has died make me free.

2. He is with me in my trouble,
   Best friend above all is HE;
   I can always depend on Jesus,
   Can HE always depend on me?

3. I can hear voice from Jesus,
   Calling me begging,
   "Go and win lost and straying";
   ? HE satisfied with me.

4. When my work on earth is finished,
   And I go to heaven,
   Oh, that I can hear HIM say,
   "I am satisfied with you."

REFRAIN:

   I am satisfied, I am satisfied,
   I am satisfied with Jesus,
   But question comes to me,
   As I think about mountain-cross,
   ? my Master satisfied with me.

Words, B. B. McKinney, 1926. Copyright 1926. Renewed 1953 Broadman Press. All rights reserved

[1] Make the sign for "save" or "salvation" with both "R" hands.

. O happy day that decided my choice[1]
On YOU, my Savior and my God!
Let my warm heart rejoice,
And tell wonderful joy all around.

. Truly finished I am saved;
I am my Lord's, and HE is mine;
HE saved me and I followed,
Happy have call divine.

. Now rest, my doubting heart,[2]
Have that peaceful rest;
Here I found wonderful thing,
Here heavenly joy[3] fills my heart.

. High heaven that hears important promise,
That promise made again shall every day hear,
Until in life's last hour I die,
And bless, in death, fellowship truly sweet.

REFRAIN:

Happy day, happy day,
When Jesus washed my sins away!
HE taught me how watch and pray,
And live happily every day;
Happy day, happy day,
When Jesus washed my sins away!

Words, Philip Doddridge, 1755; Refrain, Anonymous.

Sign "that helped me decide," if you prefer.
Sign "my long-troubled heart," if you prefer.
Make the sign for "pleasure" rather than "happy," if you prefer.

1. I love tell that story
   About not seen things above,
   About Jesus and HIS glory,
   About Jesus and HIS love:
   I love tell that story
   Because I know story true;
   That satisfies my wants
   As nothing other can satisfy.

2. I love that story;
   Truly pleasure say again
   What seems each time I tell that,
   More wonderful sweet:
   I love tell that story,
   For some people never heard
   That story about salvation
   From God's holy Word.

3. I love tell that story;
   For people who know that story best
   Seem hungry and thirsty
   For hearing that as other people:
   And when in heavenly glory
   I sing that new, new song,
   That will be same old, old story
   That I since heard truly long.

REFRAIN:

   I love tell that story,
   That will become my theme[1] in glory
   Tell that old, old story about Jesus and HIS love.

Words, Katherine Hankey, 1866.

---

[1] Make the sign for "quotation mark."

The Lily of the Valley

. I have found friend in Jesus, HE is everything to me,
HE is prettiest of ten thousand to my soul;
Flower of valley, in HIM alone I see
All I need clean and make me fully well.
In sorrow HE is my comfort, in trouble HE is my help;[1]
HE tells me every care[2] on HIM give:
HE is Flower of Valley, Bright and Morning Star,
HE is prettiest of ten thousand to my soul.

. HE all my griefs[3] has taken, and all my sorrows carried;
In temptation HE is my strong and powerful protection;[4]
I have all for HIM left, and all my sins taken
From my heart, and now HE keeps me through HIS power.
No matter all world leave me, and devil tempts me awfully,
Through Jesus I shall safely reach heaven:
HE is Flower of Valley, Bright and Morning Star,
HE is prettiest of ten thousand to my soul.

. HE will never, never leave me, not still leave me here,
While I live through faith and do HIS blessed want;
Wall as fire around me, I have nothing now fear,
With HIS bread[5] HE my hungry soul shall fill.
Then going to glory see HIS blessed face,
Where rivers as pleasure shall always roll:[6]
HE is Flower of Valley, Bright and Morning Star,
HE is prettiest of ten thousand to my soul.

Words, Charles W. Fry, 1881.

Make the sign for "stay," if you want.
Make the sign for "trouble," if you wish.
Make the sign for "sorry" if you don't know the sign for "grief."
Make the sign for "protect" or "helper."
Make the sign for "Word," if you want.
Make the sign for "flow," if you prefer.

Baptist, 1975—459   Baptist, 1956—87   Broadman—363

205   **I Will Sing of My Redeemer**

1. I will sing about my Redeemer[1]
   And HIS wonderful love to me;
   On awful cross Jesus suffered
   From punishment[2] make me free.

2. I will tell wonderful story,
   How my lost soul for saving,
   In HIS wonderful love and mercy,
   HE exchange freely gives.

3. I will praise my loving Redeemer,
   HIS winning power I will tell,
   How victory Jesus gives
   Over sin, death, and hell.

4. I will sing about my Redeemer,
   And HIS heavenly love to me;
   HE from death to life has[3] brought me,
   Son from God, with HIM continue.

REFRAIN:

   Sing, oh, sing about my Redeemer,
   With HIS blood HE bought me,
   On cross HE sealed[4] my forgiveness,[5]
   Paid debt and made me free.

Words, Philip P. Bliss, 1876.

---

[1] Make the sign for "Savior." If you like, you may make the sign for "Savior" with both "R" hand
[2] Make the sign for "punish."
[3] Make the sign for "finish."
[4] Hit the left open palm with the closed right hand, the palm facing left and the edge of the litt
   closed finger touching the left hand. It is to show "stamping" or "branding."
[5] Make the sign for "forgive" or "pardon."

. Truly[1] sweet name HIS Jesus sounds
In believer's ear!
Name comforts his sorrow, heals his wounds,[2]
And takes away his fears.

. Name makes wounded spirit well,
And quiets troubled heart;[3]
Truly bread to hungry soul,
And to tired person,[4] rest.

. Loving name! rock on which I build,
My protection[5] and hiding place;
My never failing gift, filled
With much HIS grace!

. Jesus! my shepherd, brother, friend,
My prophet, priest,[6] and king;
My Lord, my life, my way, my end,
Accept praise I bring.

Words, John Newton, 1779.

Make the sign for "how," if you prefer.
Make the sign for "sores."
Make the sign for "chest," if you wish.
Leave out the sign for "person," if you want.
Make the sign for "protect."
Make the sign for "priest" (Jewish) by placing both "P" hands over the head and then making the sign for "crown."

1. O YOU to whose all-searching[1] eye
   Darkness[2] shines as light,
   Search, prove my heart; My heart hungers[3] for YOU;
   O destroy this slavery,[4] and make me free!

2. Wash away my sins, clean my soul,
   Put my love for sins to cross;
   Make holy each thought; Let all within me
   Be clean, as YOU, my Lord, are clean.

3. If in this dark way I stray,
   Be YOU my light, be YOU my way;
   No enemy, no evil[5] must I fear,
   No harm,[6] while YOU, my God, are near.

4. Savior, where no matter YOUR steps I see,
   Not afraid, not tired, I follow YOU.
   O let YOUR hand support me continually,[7]
   And lead me to YOUR holy hill![8]

Words, Nicolaus L. von Zinzendorf, 1721; translated, John Wesley, 1738.

---

[1] Make the sign for "seek" or "look."
[2] Make the sign for "dark."
[3] Make the sign for "want" instead of "hungers," if you prefer.
[4] Make the sign for "slave." Make the sign for "these sins" instead of "this slavery," if you wish
[5] Make the sign for "bad" or "sin" (wicked).
[6] Make the sign for "tease" once. Make the sign for "danger" instead of "harm," if you want.
[7] Make the sign for "continue."
[8] Make the sign for "place" or "presence," if you wish.

Baptist, 1975—470

There's a Glad New Song

There's a Glad New Song 208

1. There is happy new song felt in my heart,
Same that angels will sing above,
And all day that really joy give;
This[1] is song about saving[2] love.

2. When my soul was lost in no-star night[3]
Where my feet never stopped stray,
At awful cost Jesus brought me light,[4]
All because of saving love.

3. When finally I stand with heavenly singers[5]
In brightness HIS throne above,
On gold shore I shall never tire
About song of saving love.

REFRAIN:

About HIS love I shall always sing
Until above I see King;
Through forever my happy song shall be
About Savior's saving love.

Words, Albert C. Fischer, *c.* 1940. © Copyright 1956 Broadman Press. All rights reserved.

Make the sign for "that" instead of "this," if you like. Also, you may leave out "is" and sign "this" or "that song about."
Make the sign for "saving" with both "R" hands for "redeeming."
Sign "When my soul was lost in sin," if you wish.
If you use "When my soul was lost in sin," then it will be better to sign "Jesus brought me salvation." Make the sign for "understanding" in place of "salvation," if you prefer.
Make the sign for "sing" with the right "C" hand, palm facing downward, when using "choir."

Baptist, 1975—471   Baptist, 1956—311

1. Walking in sunlight, all of my way;[1]
   Over mountain, through deep valley;
   Jesus has said, "I will never leave you,"
   Promise divine[2] that never can fail.

2. Dark shape around me, dark shape above me,
   Never hide my Savior and Guide;[3]
   HE is light, in HIM is no darkness;[4]
   Always I am walking near to HIS side.

3. In bright sunlight, always rejoicing,[5]
   Going my way to heaven[6] above;
   Singing HIS praises gladly I am walking,
   Walking in sunlight, sunlight HIS love.

REFRAIN:

Heavenly sunlight, heavenly sunlight,
Filling my soul with glory divine:
Hallelujah,[7] I am rejoicing,
Singing HIS praises, Jesus is mine.

Words, H. J. Zelley, 1899.

---

[1] Make the sign for "trip" or "life."
[2] Make the sign for "holy" with right "D" hand, palm facing down. Make sign for "holy," if you want.
[3] Make the sign for "leader."
[4] Make the sign for "dark."
[5] Make the sign for "happy" with one or both hands.
[6] Make the sign for "home," if you want.
[7] Make the sign for "praise-victory." Make the sign for "H" with both hands and the signs for "praise-victory" without using the "V" position, if you want.

1. Take name Jesus with you,
   Person with sorrow and trouble;
   Name will joy and comfort give you,
   Take name then where no matter you go.

2. Take name Jesus always
   As protection from every temptation;
   If temptations around you come,
   Say that holy name in prayer.

3. O sweet, important name Jesus!
   How that name thrills our souls with joy,
   When HIS loving arms put around[1] us,
   And HIS songs our hands sign.

4. At name Jesus bowing,
   Kneeling at HIS feet,
   King over kings in heaven we will crown HIM,
   When our earthly life is[2] finished.

REFRAIN:

Sweet, important name, O truly sweet!
Hope of earth and joy of heaven;
Sweet, important name, O truly sweet!
Hope of earth and joy of heaven.

Words, Lydia Baxter, 1870.

---

[1] Make the sign for "hug."
[2] Make the sign for "truly."

1. There is sunshine in my soul today,
   More glorious[1] and bright
   That glows[2] in any earth(ly) sky,
   Because Jesus is my light.

2. There is music in my soul today,
   Song to my King,
   And Jesus, listening, can hear
   Songs I cannot sing.

3. There is music in my soul today,
   Because when Lord is near,
   Bird of peace sings in my heart,
   Flowers of grace appear.

4. There is gladness[3] in my soul today,
   And hope and praise and love
   For blessings that HE gives me now,
   For joys[3] put in above.

REFRAIN:

   O there is sunshine, wonderful sunshine,
   When peaceful, happy minutes roll;
   When Jesus shows HIS smiling face,
   There is sunshine in my soul.

Words, Eliza E. Hewitt, 1887.

---

[1] Make the sign for "glory."
[2] Make the sign for "shine" if you don't know sign for "glow."
[3] Make the sign for "happy" with one or both hands.

Baptist, 1975—447   Baptist, 1956—273

Sing wonderful love HIS Jesus,
Sing HIS mercy and HIS grace:
In heavenly homes bright and happy,
HE will prepare for us a place.

While we walk Christian way,
Clouds will protect as we walk;
But when walking days are[1] finished,
Not sadness, not tear.

Let us become true and faithful,[2]
Trusting, serving every day;
Only one look at HIM in glory
Will make works during life worth.

Onward to glory before[3] us!
Soon HIS beauty we will see;
Soon heavenly doors will open;
We will walk streets pure gold.

REFRAIN:

When we all arrive heaven,
What day joy that will be!
When we all see Jesus,
We will sing and shout victory.

Words, Eliza E. Hewitt, 1898.

Make the sign for "truly."
Make the sign for "regular" with both "F" hands.
Make the sign for "presence."

1. More love to YOU, O Christ,
   More love to YOU!
   Hear YOU prayer I offer
   On bended knee;
   This is¹ my real prayer:
   More love, O Christ, to YOU,
   More love to YOU!
   More love to YOU!

2. Once earthly joy² I wished,
   Looked for peace and rest;
   Now YOU alone I seek,
   Give what is best;
   This all my prayer shall be:
   More love, O Christ, to YOU,
   More love to YOU!
   More love to YOU!

3. Then shall my last word
   Speak YOUR praise;
   This be last word
   My heart will offer;
   This still my heart's prayer will continue:
   More love, O Christ, to YOU,
   More love to YOU!
   More love to YOU!

Words, Elizabeth Prentiss, 1856.

---

¹ Make the sign for "truly."
² Make the sign for "happy" with one or both hands.

Baptist, 1975—484   Baptist, 1956—292   Broadman—21§

Face to face with Christ, my Savior,
Face to face—what[1] joy that will become,
When with great joy I see HIM,
Jesus who died for me.

Only little now I can see HIM,
With dark curtain between,
But happy day will come,
When HIS glory I will see.

What great joy in HIS presence,
When are removed[2] sorrow and pain;
When wrong ways are made right,
And hidden things will become clear.

Face to face—oh, happy minute!
Face to face—see and know;
Face to face with my Redeemer,[3]
Jesus Christ who loves me truly.

REFRAIN:

Face to face I will see HIM,
Far above starry sky;
Face to face in all HIS glory,
I will see HIM future and future.[4]

Words, Carrie E. Breck, 1898.

Make the sign for "wonderful" instead of "what," if you prefer.
Make the sign for "take away."
Make the sign for "Savior." You can sign "Savior" with both "R" hands.
You may want to sign "future" once. Be sure to keep it in rhythm with the music.

215   Take My Life, Lead Me, Lord

1. Take my life, lead me, Lord,
   Take my life, lead me, Lord,
   Make my life useful to YOU;
   Take my life, lead me, Lord,
   Take my life, lead me, Lord,
   Make my life useful to YOU.

2. Take my life, teach me, Lord,
   Take my life, teach me, Lord,
   Make my life useful to YOU;
   Take my life, teach me, Lord,
   Take my life, teach me, Lord,
   Make my life useful to YOU.

3. Here am[1] I, send me, Lord,
   Here am I, send me, Lord,
   Make my life useful to YOU;
   Here am I, send me, Lord,
   Here am I, send me, Lord,
   Make my life useful to YOU.

Words, R. Maines Rawls, 1968. © Copyright 1969 Broadman Press. All rights reserved.

[1] Make the sign for "true" or "truly."

Baptist, 1975—366

216   We Have Heard the Joyful Sound

1. We have[1] heard that happy story:
   Jesus saves! Jesus saves!
   Spread that story all around:
   Jesus saves! Jesus saves!
   Tell that story to each nation,
   Over mountain and over ocean;
   Onward! Our Lord orders;
   Jesus saves! Jesus saves!

Announce[2] over ocean:
Jesus saves! Jesus saves!
Tell to sinners far and near:
Jesus saves! Jesus saves!
Sing, you islands in ocean;
Answer again, you ocean;
Earth will continue happy:
Jesus saves! Jesus saves!

Sing above war noise:
Jesus saves! Jesus saves!
Through HIS death and eternal[3] life,
Jesus saves! Jesus saves!
Sing that story during sadness,
When your heart for mercy hungers;
Sing with victory over grave,
Jesus saves! Jesus saves!

Let wind continue spread:
Jesus saves! Jesus saves!
Let all nations now rejoice,[4]
Jesus saves! Jesus saves!
Shout salvation full and free;
Highest hill and deepest cave;
This our song about victory:
Jesus saves! Jesus saves!

Words, Priscilla Owens, c. 1882.

Make the sign for "finish."
You may make the sign for "tell."
Make the sign for "forever." You can sign "forever" with your right "E" hand, if you like.
Make a sign for "happy" with both hands.

1. Shall we gather at river,
   Where bright angel feet have[1] walked;
   With clear water forever
   Flowing near throne HIS God?

2. On side river,
   Walking feet in white water,
   We will walk and worship always,
   All happy golden day.

3. Before we reach shining river,
   Put we every burden;
   Grace our spirits will bring,[2]
   And give robe and crown.

4. Soon we will reach shining river,
   Soon our walking will stop,
   Soon our happy hearts will beat[3]
   With song of peace.

REFRAIN:

   Yes, we will gather at river,
   Beautiful, beautiful river;
   Gather with God's people at river
   That flows near throne HIS God.

Words, Robert Lowry, 1864.

---

[1] Make the sign for "finish."
[2] Make the sign for "save" in place of "bring" or "carry," if you prefer.
[3] Touch the heart area several times with the right "A" hand, palm facing self, and the left ope
palm covering the right "A" hand very slightly. Make the sign for "sing" instead of "beat,"
you prefer.

Must Jesus carry cross alone,
And all world go free?
No, there is cross for everyone,
And there is cross for me.

How many are saints[1] above,
Who once went sorrowing here!
But now they have perfect love
And joy without tear.

Consecrated[2] cross I will carry
Until death shall make me free;
And then go home my crown wear,
For there is crown for me.

O beautiful[3] street there
At Jesus' pierced[4] feet,
Joyful I will put my gold crown
And HIS name say again.

O sweet, important cross! O glorious crown!
O resurrection[5] day!
When Christ Lord from heaven comes,
And carries my soul away.

ords, Thomas Shepherd, 1693, and others.

Make the sign for "holy" with the right "S" hand, palm facing down, and end it with the sign for "er." You may use "Christians," "God's people," or "holy people" instead of "saints."
Place in front of self both "C" hands, palms facing upward. Move both hands upward while opening them into the sign for "offer." You may sign "holy" instead of "consecrated."
Make the sign for "pretty," "prettier," or "prettiest."
Make the sign for "pierce" by touching the left open palm with the tip of the right index finger which is twisted to the right. You may make the sign for "nailed" by touching the left open palm with the tip of the right index finger and then hitting the left palm with the right closed hand, the palm facing left.
Make the sign for "rising up" as if getting up from the bed and then into the air. (The left upward palm stays stationary while the right hand comes into play.)

219   There's a Land That Is Fairer than Day

1. There is land that is prettier than day,
   And through faith we can see it far;
   Because Father waits over there
   Prepare us living place there.

2. We shall sing on that beautiful shore
   Sweet song of happy Christians,[1]
   And our spirits shall sorrow no more,
   Not grief[2] for blessings join with rest.

3. To our kind Father above,
   We will offer honor with praise
   For glorious[3] gift HIS love
   And blessings that hallow[4] our days.

REFRAIN:

   In sweet future and future,[5]
   We shall meet on that beautiful shore;
   In sweet future and future,
   We shall meet on that beautiful shore.

Words, Sanford F. Bennett, 1868.

[1] Make the sign for "blessed" instead of "happy Christians," if you prefer.
[2] Make the sign for "sorry" if you don't know the sign for "grief."
[3] Make the sign for "glory."
[4] Make the sign for "holy."
[5] You may sign just "In sweet future," but be sure to keep with the music.

O That Will Be Glory

1. When all my work and trouble are[1] finished,
   And I am safe on that beautiful shore,
   Exactly[2] near loving Lord I love-worship,
   Will through years be glory for me.

2. When, through gift HIS great grace,
   I am given in heaven place,
   Exactly truly there and look on HIS face,
   Will through years be glory for me.

3. Friends will be there I have[3] loved long ago;
   Joy[4] same river around me will flow;
   Still exactly smile from my Savior I know,
   Will through years be glory for me.

REFRAIN:

O that will be glory for me,
Glory for me, glory for me,
When through HIS grace I shall look on HIS face,
That will be glory, be glory for me.

Words, Charles H. Gabriel, 1900.

---

[1] Make the sign for "truly."
[2] Make the sign for "exact."
[3] Make the sign for "finish."
[4] Make the sign for "happy" with one or both hands.

1. Come we that love LORD, And let our joys become known;
   Join in song with sweet togetherness,
   Join in song with sweet togetherness,
   And now around throne, And now around throne.

2. Let people refuse sing Who never knew God;
   But children HIS heavenly King,
   But children HIS heavenly King,
   Can speak their joys all around, Can speak their joys all around.

3. Hill of Zion[1] gives thousand holy songs,
   Before we arrive heavenly lands,
   Before we arrive heavenly lands,
   Or walk gold streets, Or walk gold streets.

4. Then let our songs continue, And every tear dry,[2]
   We are marching through God's land,
   We are marching through God's land,
   To beautiful worlds on high, To beautiful worlds on high.

REFRAIN:

We are marching to Zion, Beautiful, beautiful Zion;
We are marching up to Zion, Beautiful city of God.

Words, Isaac Watts, 1707.

---

[1] Make the sign for "Z" to be followed immediately by the sign for "town."
[2] Make the sign for "disappear," "melt," or "wiped."

Baptist, 1975—505   Baptist, 1956—308   Broadman—

When the Roll Is Called Up Yonder

When horn HIS Lord shall sound,[1] and time shall be[2] no more,[3]
And morning rises, forever,[4] bright, and pretty;
When saved people[5] on earth shall meet there on heaven's shore,
And my name is called from heaven, I will be there.

On that bright and beautiful morning when dead people in Christ
    shall rise,
And glory join with HIS resurrection[6] share;
When HIS chosen people shall gather to their home above sky,
And my name is called from heaven, I will be there.

Let us work for Jesus from morning until evening sun,
Let us talk about all HIS wonderful love and care;
Then when all life is finished, and our work on earth is done,
And my name is called from heaven, I will be there.

REFRAIN:

When my name is called from heaven,
When my name is called from heaven,
When my name is called from heaven,
When my name is called from heaven,
I will be there.

Words, James M. Black, 1893.

Make the sign for "noise."
Make the sign for "true" or "truly."
Sign "and time shall stop forever" instead of "and time shall be no more," if you prefer.
Make the sign for "forever" with the right "E" hand when using "eternal."
You may omit the sign for "people."
Make the sign for "get up" as if from bed or grave. Then move the right upside down "V" hand upward, palm facing down, as if a person is rising up into heaven or into the air.

1. O beautiful for wide sky,
   For yellow waves[1] growing,
   For purple mountain high
   Above food plenty[2] land!
   America! America!
   God give HIS grace on you,
   And crown your good with brotherhood[3]
   From sea to shining sea.

2. O beautiful for long ago people's feet,
   Whose hard, strong feeling force
   Way for freedom open
   Across dry land!
   America! America!
   God heals[4] your every wrong,
   Strengthen[5] your soul in self-control,
   Your freedom in law.

3. O beautiful for brave people proved
   In freedom fight,
   Who more than self their country loved,
   And mercy more than life!
   America! America!
   May God your gold make clean,
   Until all success become great,[6]
   And every gain divine.

4. O beautiful for country lover's dream
   That sees, beyond years,
   Your white cities show,
   Seen clearly through people's tears!
   America! America!
   God give HIS grace on you,
   And crown your good with brotherhood
   From sea to shining sea.

Words, Katharine Lee Bates, 1893.

---

[1] Move both upright, spread hands, palms facing each other, to right, then to left, and again to right. This is a picture of the wheat waving to and fro in the wind.

Make the sign for "growing" instead of "food plenty," if you want.
Make the sign for "brother" to be followed with the sign for "cooperate."
Make the sign for "straight" instead of "heal," if you wish.
Make the sign for "strength," "make strong," or "make sure."
Make the sign for "wonderful" or "excellent."

Baptist, 1975—508   Baptist, 1956—489   Broadman—39

We Shall Walk Through the Valley   224

1. We shall walk through valley in peace;
   We shall walk through valley in peace;
   Because Jesus HIMSELF will be[1] our Leader.
   We shall walk through valley in peace.

2. There will be no sorrow there;
   There will be no sorrow there;
   Because Jesus HIMSELF will be our Leader.
   There will be no sorrow there.

3. We shall meet our loving people there;
   We shall meet our loving people there;
   Because Jesus HIMSELF will be our Leader.
   We shall meet our loving people there.

4. We shall meet our Savior there;
   We shall meet our Savior there;
   Because Jesus HIMSELF will be our Leader.
   We shall meet our Savior there.

Words, Anonymous.

Make the sign for "true" or "truly."

Baptist, 1975—501

1. My eyes have seen glory coming HIS Lord;
   HE is stepping on[1] wine where grapes full anger are kept;
   HE has let awful lightning from HIS awful sword;
   HIS truth is marching on.

2. I have see HIM in watch-fire with one hundred tents around;
   Soldiers built HIM altar[2] in evening wetness;[3]
   I can read HIS right judgment through low and bright fires;
   HIS day is marching on.

3. HE has blown horn that will never sound retreat;[4]
   HE is judging hearts their people before HIS judgment seat;
   O be fast, my soul, answer HIM! Be happy, my feet!
   Our God is marching on.

4. In beauty flowers, Christ was born across sea,
   With glory in HIS life that changes you and me;
   As HE died make people holy, Let us live make people free,
   While God is marching on.

5. HE is coming as glory of morning on wave;
   HE is wisdom to strong, HE is honor to brave;
   Truly world shall become HIS foot place, and soul doing wrong
    HIS slave.
   Our God is marching on.

REFRAIN:

 Glory! glory, hallelujah! Glory! glory, hallelujah!
 Glory! glory, hallelujah! Our God is marching on.

Words, Julia Ward Howe, 1861.

---

[1] Make the sign for "crush."
[2] Bring to touch both thumbs of the "A" hands, palm facing downward. Move both hands away
from each other horizontally and then vertically with both palms facing each other.
[3] Make sign for "wet."

Rotate both open hands backward in a counterclockwise motion as if showing the loss of ground inch by inch or foot by foot. Ask the deaf person or another person to help you with this sign if you don't know the sign(s) for "retreat" as in war.

Baptist, 1975—510   **Baptist, 1956—488**

I'm Not Ashamed   226

I am[1] not ashamed accept my Lord,
Or defend HIS name,
Keep honor HIS Word,
Glory HIS cross.

Jesus, my God! I know HIS name,
HIS name is all my trust;
Not will HE make my soul ashamed,
Not let my hope be lost.

Strong same HIS throne HIS promise stands,
And HE can really keep
What I have[2] given to HIS hands
Until decided time.

Then will HE accept my worth-nothing name
Before[3] HIS Father's face,
And in new Jerusalem[4]
Give my soul place.

Words, Isaac Watts, 1707.

Make the sign for "true" or "truly."
Make the sign for "finish."
Make the sign for "presence" or "in front."
Make the sign for "J" + "town."

Baptist, 1975—450

1. My country, true about you,
   Sweet land freedom,
   About you I sing:
   Land where my fathers died,
   Land here first people's pride,[1]
   From every mountain
   Let freedom ring!

2. My home country, you,[2]
   Land noble free,
   Your name I love:
   I love your rocks and valley,
   Your trees and pretty hills;
   My heart with happy thrills
   As that above.

3. Let music[3] spread air,
   And ring from all trees
   Sweet freedom's song:
   Let people start singing;
   Let all that breathe join;
   Let rocks their quiet break,
   Sound continue.

4. Our father's God, to YOU,
   Giver of freedom,
   To YOU we sing:
   Long let our land continue bright
   With freedom's holy light;
   Protect us through YOUR power,
   Great God, our King!

Words, Samuel F. Smith, 1831.

---

[1] Use "Land about first ago people wandering (straying) with pride," if you prefer.
[2] Sign "My born, grown up country, you," if you like.
[3] Make the sign for "song." You can make a sign for "song" with the right "M" hand, palm facin
down.

O Jesus, I Have Promised

. O Jesus, I have[1] promise Serve YOU to end;
Be[2] YOU forever near me, My Master[3] and my friend;
I shall not fear war If YOU are near my side,
Not stray from pathway[4] If YOU will be my leader.

. O Jesus, YOU have promised To all who follow YOU,
That where YOU are in glory There shall YOUR servants[5] be;
And, Jesus, I have promised Serve YOU to end;
O give me grace follow My Master and my friend!

. O let me feel YOU near me! World is always near;
I see things that attract,[6] Tempting noises I hear;
My enemy is always near me, Around me and within;[7]
But, Jesus, Come YOU nearer And protect my soul from sin.

. O let me hear YOU speaking In voice clear and quiet,
Above mixed[8] feeling Complaining from self want.
O speak comfort me, Hurry or control!
O speak, and make me listen, YOU protector[9] of my soul! Amen.

Words, John E. Bode, 1868.

Make the sign for "finish."
Make the sign for "true" or "truly."
Make the sign for "Savior" or "Lord" if you don't know the sign for "Master."
Make the sign for "way" with both "P" hands. Make the sign for "way," if you like.
Make the sign for "people" instead of "servants," if you want.
Make the sign for "interest" or "interesting" if you don't know the sign for "attract."
Make the sign for "inside" near the heart or chest area.
Make the signs for "storms of feeling," if you want. "Mixed" is used to show "confused feeling"
or "troubled emotion."
Make the sign for "protect," ending with the sign for "er" as in "teacher."

229   I Have Decided to Follow Jesus

1. I have[1] decided follow Jesus,
   I have decided follow Jesus,
   I have decided follow Jesus,
   No turning around, no turning around.

2. No matter none go with me I still will follow,
   No matter none go with me I still will follow,
   No matter none go with me I still will follow,
   No turning around, no turning around.

3. My cross I will carry until I see Jesus,
   My cross I will carry until I see Jesus,
   My cross I will carry until I see Jesus,
   No turning around, I will follow HIM.

Words, st. 1, 2, as sung by the Garo Christians; st. 3, John Clark. © Copyright 1959 Broadman Press. All rights reserved.

---

[1] Make the sign for "finish."

Baptist, 1975—191

230   I've Got Peace Like a River

1. I have[1] got peace same river,
   I have got peace same river,
   I have got peace same river in my soul.
   I have got river in my soul.

2. I have got love same river,
   I have got love same river,
   I have got love same river in my soul.
   I have got river in my soul.

3. I have got joy[2] same river,
   I have got joy same river,
   I have got joy same river in my soul.
   I have got river in my soul.

Words, Traditional Spiritual.

Make the sign for "finish."
Make the sign for "happy" with one or both hands.

Baptist, 1975—458

The Star-Spangled Banner 231

1. O say, can you see, through morning sunrise bright,
   What truly proudly we welcomed[1] evening last light,
   Whose broad stripes and bright stars, through awful war,
   Over walls we watched, were very bravely flying?
   And rockets red light, bombs burst in air
   Gave proof through night that our flag was still there.
   O say, really that Star-sprinkled Flag still wave
   Over land of free and home of brave?

2. O, in this way be that always when free men shall stand
   Between their loved homes and war's destruction;[2]
   Blessed with victory and peace, may heaven saved land
   Praise God that had made and kept us nation!
   Then beat[3] we must, when our fight that is right;
   And this be our theme:[4] "In God is our trust!"
   And Star-sprinkled Flag in victory shall wave
   Over land of free and home of brave.

Words, Francis Scott Key, 1814.

Make the signs for "salute at," if you wish.
Make the sign for "destroy." Make the sign for "empty" in place of "destroy," if you want.
Make the sign for "win" instead of "beat," if you want.
Make the sign for "quotation mark."

Baptist, 1975—512   Baptist, 1956—486   Broadman—457

232　My Singing Is a Prayer

1. My singing is prayer, O Lord,
   Prayer with thanks and praise;
   In song, Lord, I worship YOU;
   YOUR beauty fills my days.

2. I give my talents, Lord, to YOU,
   My mind and heart and voice,
   Because YOU alone are worthy, Lord;
   In YOU I really rejoice.

3. Accept worship from my heart,
   Accept my song, too:
   Help me live always for YOU,
   Lord, keep me strong and true.

4. O bless me, Lord, and help me sing
   YOUR love truly full and free;
   And bless all who listen, Lord,
   Help them worship YOU.

Words, Novella D. Preston, 1964. © Copyright 1964 Broadman Press. All rights reserved.

Baptist, 1975—412

233　Children of the Heavenly Father

1. Children HIS heavenly Father
   Safely in HIS presence gather;
   Bird in nest not star in heaven
   Wonderful protection was given.

2. God HIS children really care and feed;
   In HIS holy presence they grow,
   From all sinful things HE keeps them;
   In HIS powerful arms HE carries them.

3. Not life or death shall anytime
   From Lord HIS children separate;
   To them HIS grace HE shows,
   And their sorrows all HE knows.

4. No matter HE gives or HE takes,
   God HIS children never leaves;
   HIS loving purpose only
   Keep them pure and holy. Amen.

Words, Caroline V. Sandell-Berg, 1858; translated, Ernest W. Olson, 1925.

Baptist, 1975—207

Sing to the Lord of Harvest   234

1. Sing to Lord of harvest,
   Sing songs with love and praise;
   With happy hearts and voices
   YOUR praises offer.

2. Through HIM changing months
   In times of growing come;
   O sing to Lord of harvest,
   Song with happy love.

3. Bring to HIS holy altar
   Gifts HIS goodness gave,
   Gold growing from harvest,
   Souls HE died save.

4. Your hearts put down before HIM
   When at HIS feet you kneel;
   And with your lives love-worship HIM
   Who gave HIS life for all.

Words, John S. B. Monsell, 1866.

Baptist, 1975—232

INDEXES

Topical Index

Index of First Lines and Titles

Titles are in caps and small caps; first lines in lower case type

250